# CONTENT

This Guide is arranged in sections relating to the nine local authority Districts in the historic geographical county of Lincolnshire. Within each District the sites are listed according to contiguity, with a few exceptions, and to help locate particular sites there are two indexes at the end of the Guide, one listing sites alphabetically by type and one by place. Each entry in the Guide has a letter and number that relates to the map at the beginning of each District. Each record gives a site's name followed by a location and a National Grid reference to aid more precise location.

The selection of sites is subjective and by no means exhaustive, but has been made on the basis of sites where there is still something of historical interest to see from accessible places.

The inclusion of sites in the Guide does not imply automatic public access. Some indication of access is given, but when in doubt it is always courteous to ask permission to enter a site.

This booklet is published by the Society for Lincolnshire History and Archaeology, which was formed in 1974 by the amalgamation of earlier societies whose history goes back to 1844. The Society includes an industrial archaeology team whose members have compiled the information in this booklet.

Whilst we have attempted to ensure that the details in this Guide are correct at the time of going to press, neither the authors nor the publishers can accept liability for any loss or damage resulting from inaccuracy.

© Copyright rests with the contributors and the Society for Lincolnshire History and Archaeology.

Maps are reproduced from the Ordnance Survey map by permission of Ordnance Survey on behalf of The Controller of Her Majesty's Stationary Office, © Crown Copyright 100042712.

COVER ILLUSTRATIONS *front:* Heckington Windmill, with signal box of Heckington Station in foreground (NK36, NK37), FHM, see pages 53 and 54.
*back:* Hydraulic Tower, Grimsby Royal Dock in foreground (NE6, NE8), KR, see page 42.

ISBN: 0 903582 20 1

### Edited by Neil Wright

Horkstow Bridge, North Lincolnshire (NL16), see page 59 -KR.

## THE CONTEXT OF LINCOLNSHIRE'S INDUSTRIAL ARCHAEOLOGY

The county of Lincolnshire is second only to Yorkshire in size and extends nearly a hundred miles from the Isle of Axholme to the Norfolk border. Yet it is still largely unknown territory to many people. Its reputation for flatness mainly applies to the fens. Elsewhere the county has areas of higher land sloping gently down from west to east before meeting low wide valleys and then a steeper scarp slope. Along the western edge of the county are the Trent and upper Witham valleys, facing the scarp of the Lincoln Edge. Then to the east are the higher lands of the Heath sloping down to the Ancholme Valley, the lower Witham valley and the Fens, and east of those river valleys are the Lincolnshire Wolds, rising in places up to 500 ft, and beyond them the coastal Marsh which curves round to join the Fens at Wainfleet.

Lincolnshire's main role in the industrial revolution was as a supplier of food and raw materials, grown on the county's rich acres, to the industrial areas which could be reached by sea, river or by land. But its industrial archaeology extends beyond that to include the means of better producing food and crops, processing some of it, moving it, and meeting the needs of the county's own people. A number of Victorian engineering firms produced agricultural machinery and grew to be of world significance. In the 19th century, iron ore was rediscovered at Scunthorpe, and a number of other sites near Lincoln, Grantham and Caistor.

The fens occupy the south-east corner of the county and in these and other low lying areas such as the Coastal Marsh, the Ancholme valley and the Isle of Axholme there are extensive systems of wide and deep "drains" and pumping stations to keep the land free from flooding. The network of drains in the East, West and Wildmore Fens north of Boston (40,000 acres) were engineered by John Rennie in 1802-12 at great expense. At New Bolingbroke can still be seen John Parkin- **1**

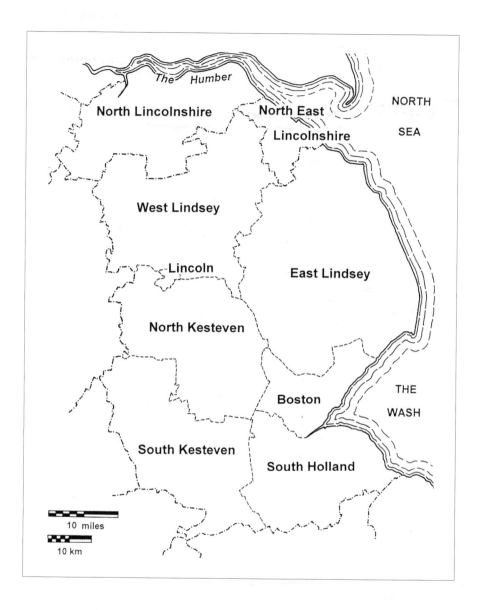

son's attempt in 1824-26 to create a new town in the heart of the West Fen.   Remains of wind-powered pumping engines can be seen at Amber Hill and Dyke, steam engines with machinery at Dogdyke and Pinchbeck Marsh, and remains of pumphouses at Pode Hole, Timberland, Owston Ferry and elsewhere, some with diesel and electric powered pumps.   In many parts of the county are the remains of planned farms created in the era of High Farming in the third quarter of the 19th century.   Christopher Turnor (1809-86) had large estates in the Wragby and Stoke Rochford areas in the mid 19th century and probably built more farmsteads, cottages and other buildings on his estate than any other contemporary landowner, perhaps the best example being Manor Farm, Kirmond le Mire.

There were once hundreds of windmills and watermills in the county. Windmill technology reached its peak in 19th century Lincolnshire and the county now has more restored working windmills than any other county. Apart from the wooden post mill at Wrawby the other working mills are multi-sailed brick tower mills with the distinctive Lincolnshire ogee cap, and in 2000 work started on the restoration of the giant Moulton Mill, the tallest surviving tower in the country, to working order. As well as its windmills, the county had some watermills in the uplands of Kesteven and the Wolds of East Lindsey and a few survive, as at Tealby, Sleaford and Alvingham.

Lincolnshire was a major producer of barley, and maltings survived until recently in most market towns, particularly around railway lines and stations. The greatest industrial monument in the county is the massive eight-block maltings at Sleaford built 1899-1905 for Bass, Ratcliffe & Gretton of Burton on Trent. Lincolnshire's own breweries were smaller and few buildings remain, apart from Bateman's of Wainfleet. Other local products included feathers, which were processed in the distinctive Trinity Street factory in Boston, and sugar beet processed at various factories until the late 20th century. Flax was produced in parts of the Isle of Axholme and the Fens but there was no textile industry in Lincolnshire despite a few unsuccessful attempts to set up small mills in the late 18th century.

During the 19th century, and particularly after railways arrived in the late 1840s, engineering firms arose in the market towns to produce agricultural machinery. Some achieved international status and great size as they exported steam engines and threshing machines to grain-growing areas around the world. Firms such as Tuxford & Sons, Hornsby & Sons, Clayton & Shuttleworth, Robey & Co., William Foster & Co., Marshall & Sons and Ruston, Proctor & Co. brought world-wide fame to Lincolnshire engineering and some made millionaires of their owners. Tuxford's produced the first portable steam threshing set, Hornsby's made the first "diesel" engine (before Dr Diesel), and Foster's made the first British tank in World War I. Of some firms all trace has disappeared but there are still substantial remains of great engineering works in Lincoln and Gainsborough.

Water transport has always been important in Lincolnshire with several ports and small havens around the coast and along the main rivers. The Welland Navigation was extended to Stamford as a canal in the 17th century, arguably the first post-Roman canal in the country, and in the 18th century and early 19th century other rivers were improved and a few new canals created to give smaller market towns better transport. These waterways served the internal needs of the county and only the Fossdyke and the Grantham canals were linked to the national canal system. Some of the early waterways were engineered by John Grundy of Spalding, and then William Jessop was involved in canals created in the canal mania of the 1790s. He was followed by John Rennie who worked on several Lincolnshire projects in the first two decades of the 19th century. Within the fens the fen drains were also used for navigation and formed a distinct and extensive network. At Boston, Tetney, South Ferriby, Keadby and Torksey tidal locks were built where the inland waterways interfaced with tidal waters. Early warehouses and wharves can still be seen in the coastal and river ports of Boston, Gainsborough, Spalding and Sutton Bridge.

The lack of roads on the pre-enclosure Lincoln Heath led to the erection of the land lighthouse, known as Dunston Pillar, in 1751. The pillar still stands to a good height and part of the Coade-stone statue of George III, erected in place of the lantern in 1810, can be seen at Lincoln Castle. The major roads in the county were turnpiked in the late 18th century but in total Lincolnshire had a smaller proportion of its roads turnpiked than many other counties. This was perhaps because of the generally easier terrain, with gentle hills and slopes rather than deep valleys and high hills. At the same time toll bridges were erected at Dunham, Gainsborough, Tattershall, Fosdyke and Sutton Bridge to replace ferries or fords. Turnpike trusts were abolished in the late 19th century and though many tollhouses were destroyed there are still a few that survive as at Stamford and

Hallington. Most toll-bridges were also freed from tolls, with Dunham Bridge over the River Trent and the Humber Bridge being the only exceptions in this county.

The first railways reached Lincolnshire in 1846 when the MR opened branches to Lincoln and Stamford on the county's western border. But it was the GNR and the MSLR that were to dominate the county's rail network. They built the first main lines through Lincolnshire, the GNR in the southern two thirds and the MSLR in the northern third of the county. The core of the network was opened in 1848. GNR lines went from Peterborough through Boston to Lincoln, and from Boston through Alford and Louth to Grimsby. The MSLR main line entered the county at Gainsborough and went east to Barton on Humber, with a branch to Grimsby, where the railway company built vast docks over the next few years. Even when small local companies built branch lines (such as the Lincoln and Louth line through the Wolds) they were soon absorbed by the two main players. The GNR resisted other major companies entering its territory, and in the cases of the M&GN and the GN&GE only withdrew opposition in return for joint involvement. The first closures started in the 1930s and the county lost most of its network on 5th October 1970, the infamous Dr. Beeching being commemorated in a street name next to the former Alford Station. Even where lines have closed there are still some surviving stations, as in Alford and Louth.

Ancaster stone has been used for building for many centuries, and can be seen in many buildings in the SW of the county. Ironstone had been worked in Roman times but was then forgotten until 1860 when its properties were rediscovered in the north of the county and the large new town of Scunthorpe was formed out of five small rural villages. Gypsum was dug on the Isle of Axholme but left few remains. Chalk pits can be seen in many parts of the Wolds, there are extensive water-filled pits in the river valleys where sand and gravel have been extracted, and there is a large cement factory at South Ferriby and limeworks at Kirton in Lindsey but not much else can be seen of mineral extraction.

There are a great many military sites throughout Lincolnshire, and the county is sometimes known as Bomber County because of the number of RAF bases here in World War II. These and other military sites are mostly outside the scope of this Guide, though the earliest known bomb shelter, at Cleethorpes, is included.

Main Railways in Lincolnshire

The railways referred to in the text are as follows:

BR – British Railways
GCR – Great Central Railway (previously MSLR)
GN&GEJR – Great Northern and Great Eastern Joint Railway
GNR – Great Northern Railway
LNER – London and North Eastern Railway
M&GNJR – Midland and Great Northern Joint Railway
MR – Midland Railway
MSLR – Manchester, Sheffield and Lincolnshire Railway (Later GCR)
SYR – South Yorkshire Railway

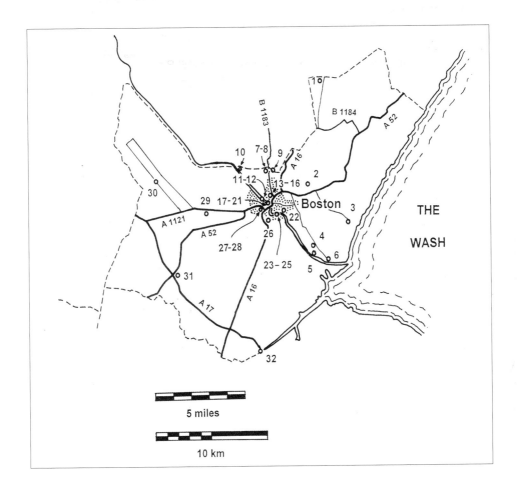

Boston District is in the northern part of the Lincolnshire Fens. It includes the town of Boston and a number of villages to the east and west, and lies close to the north shore of the Wash. As the fens were finally drained and enclosed in the late 18th century and early 19th century the port of Boston enjoyed a major revival to export grain to London by coastal shipping, to Yorkshire via the Humber, and to Lancashire and the Midlands via the R Witham and the Fossdyke Navigation. The area includes a rare wind-powered drainage pump at Amber Hill as well as the steam-powered Lade Bank Pumping Station. The complexities of fen drainage are well demonstrated by the structures at Cowbridge. In Boston town are some remains of port buildings and the later Dock, as well as the Maud Foster Windmill and other transport and food-processing buildings. Boston had two of the first agricultural engineering firms in the county, Howden and Tuxford, and parts of their premises still remain.

## BN1 LADE BANK PUMPING STATION, OLD LEAKE

*On west bank of the Hobhole Drain, 6 miles north of Haltoft End on A52*
TF 379546
*Access: View from public road*

Built in 1867 when shrinking of the peat in the East Fen (due to efficient drainage) lowered the land surface and the water had to be pumped into the higher southern half of the Hobhole Drain. Diesel pumps installed in 1940 but the Victorian building and chimney still remain. The 14 mile long navigable drain had been excavated in 1802-06 as part of John Rennie's scheme to drain these fens. Alongside the pumping station are the remains of a lock.

## BN2 BAKERS BRIDGE, FISHTOFT

*2 miles east of Boston, ½ mile north of Haltoft End on A52*
TF 362459
*Access: from public road*

One of a series of small attractive brick bridges over the Cowbridge Drain, dated from c1805. It is a typical example of bridges of the area, over the Hobhole Drain and other fenland drains.

## BN3 COASTAL RESORT, FREISTON SHORE

*3 miles east of Boston, on shore of Wash*
TF 397424
*Access: view from public road*

In Georgian times this was a coastal resort with two inns and lodgings in farmhouses and cottages. It was by-passed by the railways and did not grow, but one inn remains, converted to mews, and the other only closed about forty years ago. In the 20thC the marsh outside the sea bank was reclaimed but more recently it has been returned to the sea.

## BN4 NUNN'S BRIDGE, FISHTOFT

*2 miles south east of Boston, on road to North Sea Camp*
TF 367416
*Access: from public road*

Britain's first in-situ prestressed concrete bridge, utilising post-tensioning of the reinforced concrete beams. It was built in 1947 with a single span of 72ft (22m). Designed by G E Buchner with L G Mouchel & Partners.

## BN5 HOBHOLE SLUICE, FISHTOFT

*2½ miles south-east of Boston, at end of Hobhole Drain*
TF 364399
*Access: From public footpath*

This sluice is at the end of Hobhole Drain which was a central feature of John Rennie's new drainage scheme for the East, West and Wildmore Fens. The sluice built in 1805-6 and repaired in 1888 has been replaced by a pumping station and new cut constructed in 1957.

## BN6 CUT END, FISHTOFT

*3 miles south-east of Boston, at end of road to North Sea Camp*
TF 372394 to TF 397392
*Access: Public footpath along top of the north bank*

The new outfall channel for the R Witham, 2 miles long, was excavated in 1880-84 to improve the drainage of the river and allow larger vessels to reach Boston where a dock was then being built.

### BN7 FOOTBRIDGE, COWBRIDGE, FISHTOFT

*2 miles north of Boston, off road to Horncastle*
TF 327471
*Access: Crossed by public footpath*

One of three matching footbridges cast at Butterley (Derbyshire) in 1811 and erected over the Maud Foster Drain. They were designed either by John Rennie or William Jessop. Vauxhall Bridge went in 1924 but Hospital Bridge still remains at Boston (BN 13).

### BN8 LOCK, COWBRIDGE, FISHTOFT

*2 miles north of Boston, adjacent B1183*
TF 328472
*Access: From adjacent public road*

This gives access between the West Fen Drain, Maud Foster Drain, and three other navigable drains which converge at Cowbridge. It is stone built, c1805, with a sluice alongside, and has a guillotine at the north end; the other gates are opened by winches. At TF 331470 there was another lock, which has been filled in and the bridge over it demolished, that gave access via the Cowbridge and Hob Hole drains to the East Fen.

### BN9 AQUEDUCT, COWBRIDGE, FISHTOFT

*2 miles north of Boston, off road to Horncastle*
TF 330474
*Access: by public footpath across Golf Course*

This carries the waters of the Stonebridge Drain over those of the Cowbridge Drain, but it is almost an inverted siphon because the waters of the two drains are virtually on the same level. By John Rennie c1805, using Aberdeen granite!

### BN10 ANTON'S GOWT LOCK, FISHTOFT

*2½ miles north-west of Boston*
TF 300475
*Access: On public footpath to river bank from public road*

This gives access to the navigable drains on the East, West and Wildmore fens which were drained 1802-12 by John Rennie. This lock, like those on the Witham at Bardney and Lincoln, has unusual curved gates. The GNR's Lincolnshire Loop Line went right over the top of this lock, but the bridge was removed after the closure of the railway line in 1963. The lock was built without parliamentary sanction (not in the Act).

**7**

BN8: Lock, Cowbridge, Fishtoft - NRW

## BN11 GRAND SLUICE, BOSTON
*¼ mile north of Boston Stump*
TF 323445
*Access: From road over sluice and adjacent river bank*
This Sluice across the R Witham was built 1764-66 by Langley Edwards as part of a scheme devised by Edwards, John Grundy and John Smeaton to improve the drainage of the fens above Boston. The sluice consists of four arches with a tidal lock, enlarged to its present size in 1881, under the eastern arch. The upstream sluice gates were modernised in 1979/82. Witham Town developed here as Boston's inland port. The railway bridge at the Grand Sluice was built by GNR in 1885 to replace their original timber bridge of 1848.

BN11: Lock and warehouses at Grand Sluice, Boston – NRW

## BN12 GRAND SLUICE IRON WORKS, BOSTON
*In Witham Town, 200 yards north of Grand Sluice; house on river bank*
TF 322445
*Access: Can be seen from street*
Fragments remain of William Howden's foundry of 1803, the first foundry in Lincolnshire, including his own house on the river bank with lots of heavy ironwork decoration.

## BN13 HOSPITAL BRIDGE, BOSTON
*Adjacent to Horncastle Road (B1183), ½ mile northeast of Boston Stump*
TF 332448
*Access: Crossed by public footpath*
One of three matching footbridges cast at Butterley (Derbyshire) in 1811 and erected over the Maud Foster Drain which John Rennie was then widening. Designed either by Rennie or William Jessop, with an extremely flat arch. Vauxhall Bridge was replaced by a road bridge in 1924 (and rebuilt c2002) but the other footbridge at Cowbridge (BN7) still remains.

BN13: Hospital Bridge, Boston – NRW

## BN14 MAUD FOSTER WINDMILL, BOSTON

*Willoughby Road, ½ mile north-east of town centre*
TF 332447
*Access: open Wed, Sat, Sun, also Thur. & Fri in July and August and Bank Holiday Mondays. (01205) 352188*

Tower mill built in 1819 for brothers Thomas and Isaac Reckitt from Wainfleet; six-storeys high with five-sails. Preserved by a family trust in the 1950s and restored to full working order in the 1990s.

## BN15 BARGATE BRIDGE, BOSTON

*Spilsby Road, end of Wide Bargate*
TF 332446
*Access: Crossed by public highway*

John Rennie's original bridge of c1810 over the Maud Foster Drain was widened c1980 by taking down and re-erecting the southern façade. Just north of Bargate Bridge are the Corn Steps which were used by passengers on the market packet boats which travelled the navigable drains until the early 20thC.

## BN16 TURNPIKE BOUNDARY MARKER, BOSTON

*In Wide Bargate, in front of Cammack's shop*
TF 329443
*Access: Set in pavement*

Still surviving in the pavement in front of Cammack's shop is an unusual plate to indicate the limit of the turnpike trust's responsibility for repairing part of Wide Bargate.

## BN17 TOWN BRIDGE, BOSTON

*Town centre*
TF 327440
*Access: Crossed by public highway*

Built 1913 to replace John Rennie's bridge of 1803-06. Designed by John J Webster, MinstCE, Engineer.

BN17: Town Bridge, Boston – NRW

## BN18 PACKHOUSE QUAY, BOSTON

*200 yds south of town centre*
TF 328439
*Access: public access onto car park above quay*

Principal quay of the port until the Dock opened in 1884; surrounded by warehouses of which only a few survive. The stone and brick wall of the quay was built 1814-15 on a curved line proposed by John Rennie. See also Doughty Quay (BN21).

## BN19 BRITANNIA OIL MILL, BOSTON

*On Packhouse Quay, at junction with Spain Lane*
TF 328439
*Access: Can be seen from street*

This former oil seed crushing mill at the corner of South Street and Spain Lane was built c1850 and was later used as a seed store. Converted into apartments in 1990s.

**9**

BN20: Warehouses in South Square, Boston - NRW

## BN20 WAREHOUSES, SOUTH STREET AND SOUTH SQUARE, BOSTON

*200 yds south of town centre*
*TF 328438*
*Access: Can be viewed from street*
The Sam Newsom Music Centre at the southern end of Packhouse Quay was formed in 1978 out of a warehouse which had been built in stages during the 18thC and 19thC. The conversion by Lincolnshire County Council retains much of its external appearance and some internal features. Beyond in South Square are two granaries converted to apartments in the 1990s. The one built of stone and brick is dated 1810 and the other is perhaps a little earlier. Also remaining in the Square are four fine 18thC and 19thC merchants' houses.

## BN21 DOUGHTY QUAY, BOSTON

*High Street, 300 yds south of town centre*
*TF 327438*
*Access: View from car park above quay*
This was the main quay on the west bank of the Haven, with a curving wall similar to Packhouse Quay (BN 18) now lost behind 1950s piling. At the north end is a tall and slender warehouse of c1810, with a low pitched roof and overhanging gables.

## BN22 BOSTON AND SKIRBECK IRON WORKS

*Fishtoft Road, mile south-east of centre of Boston*
*TF 336432*
*Access: Can be seen from public roads*
William Tuxford and his sons ran one of the principal iron works in Lincolnshire from c1837 to 1885. The business was small but they were very inventive, and in 1842 produced the

BN22: Tuxford's Boston and Skirbeck Iron Works, 1856

BN22: Former Office,
Tuxford's Boston and Skirbeck
Iron Works, Boston – NRW

first set of portable threshing machine and steam engine. They exported portable and traction engines worldwide. Fragments of their buildings survive, including the 2-storey former office block east of Mount Bridge. The machinery, cap and sails of their tower windmill were removed to Heckington in 1891 (see NK36).

## BN23 MAUD FOSTER SLUICE, BOSTON

*Off Fishtoft Road, mile south-east of town centre*
TF 335431
*Access: From road along drain bank.*
Designed by John Rennie as part of drainage of East, West and Wildmore Fens. Built 1806/ 07 where Maud Foster Drain entered tidal Witham. Contractor John Pinkerton. Upstream sluice gates modernised and mechanised in 1985.

## BN24 BOSTON DOCK

*¾ mile south of town centre*
TF 332431
*Access: No public access, can be seen from London Road*
The trade of the port was considerably revived after this dock was built in 1882-84, to designs of William Wheeler, the Borough Surveyor, and the channel to the Wash was straightened and deepened. Few original buildings survive around the 7-acre basin except the now disused Hydraulic Engine House. The entrance lock is 300ft by 50ft (91.4m by 15.2m) but there are plans afoot to enlarge it for modern shipping.

## BN25 SWING BRIDGE, BOSTON

*½ mile south of town centre, off London Road*
TF 326430
*Access: View from adjacent public road*
This single-track railway bridge of 1882/84 by Handysides of Derby connected Boston Dock to the GNR lines and goods yards. It was originally hand-operated and was converted to elec-

BN25: Swing Bridge,
Boston – NRW

tricity in 1981. It is a 129ft (39.3m) superstructure pivoted on a central pier. The polygonal signal box at the Swing Bridge was built in 1893.

### BN26 BLACK SLUICE, BOSTON
*¾ mile south of town centre, off London Road*
TF 327428
*Access: From road over sluice*
Original sluice c1640, Langley Edwards sluice 1765 south of it rebuilt by Cubitt 1846/50, improved 1960s. Tidal outfall for the South Forty Foot Drain. Lock destroyed when C20 pumping station built.

### BN27 TRINITY STREET FEATHER FACTORY, BOSTON
*½ mile west of town centre, close to railway station*
TF 323440
*Access: can be seen from street*
Built in 1877 by Mrs F S Anderson & Company for the purifying of feathers for pillow cases and other products. This is the last surviving 19thC building of this ancient fenland industry. Now flats.

### BN28 GREAT NORTHERN RAILWAY – PASSENGER STATION, CIVIL ENGINEEER'S YARD AND SIGNAL BOX, BOSTON
*½ mile west of town centre*
TF 321438
*Access: Passenger station in use; other buildings can be seen from street*
Passenger Station built 1850, new ticket office 1911 (now café), old entrance restored 1991-93. Civil Engineer's Workshops south of Sleaford Road built by GNR in 1890s were converted to modern offices by East Midlands

Electricity Board in 1970s and are now a fitness centre. Signal box is typical GNR.

### BN29 HUBBERT'S BRIDGE, KIRTON
*3 miles west of Boston, off A1121*
TF 270437
*Access: Public road (B1192) over bridge*
This bridge of c1850 replaced the original one which carried a turnpike road across the navigable South Forty Foot Drain. A settlement grew up here, with a wharf and a warehouse beside the drain, and in 1859 a single track railway, later doubled and now again reduced to single track except in the station, was built along the north bank.

### BN30 DRAINAGE ENGINES, AMBER HILL
*Adjacdent to minor road on Holland Fen, 6 miles west of Boston*
TF 229460 and TF 234455
*Access: One in private garden, one adjacent to public road*
The engine at Spinney Farm has a brick tower, internal gearing and its scoop wheel, though its cap and sails were evidently removed when it was converted to be driven by an external steam engine (portable or traction). If this was originally wind-driven, as is generally accepted, then it is an unusual survival because most 18thC wind drainage engines were replaced by steam engines on the same site (cf Dogdyke (EL73)). About half mile south (at TF 234455) the scoop wheel and channel remain of another such engine.

BN27: Trinity Street Feather Factory – NRW

## BN31 TURNPIKE MILE POST, SWINESHEAD

*In cul-de-sac south of eastern roundabout at Drayton*
TF 242388
*Access: at side of road*

The manufacturer's name – Howden of Boston – can clearly be seen on top of this post at Drayton. Other posts still remain on roads south, east and west of the two roundabouts at Drayton.

## BN32 FOSDYKE BRIDGE

*7 miles south of Boston, on main A17*
TF 318322
*Access: Public road (A17) crosses the bridge*

In 1812-15 banks were built to reclaim most of the Welland estuary and the river was confined to a narrow channel crossed by a swing bridge. The first wooden bridge by John Rennie was replaced by an iron one in 1910-11, probably the last bridge to be built by Handysides of Derby, and the present bridge was erected in 1988/89. During 19thC a hamlet developed around the bridge, including two public houses, a harbour master's house, coastguard cottages and a wharf which is still in use.

BN31: Turnpike Mile Post,
Swineshead – NRW

**13**

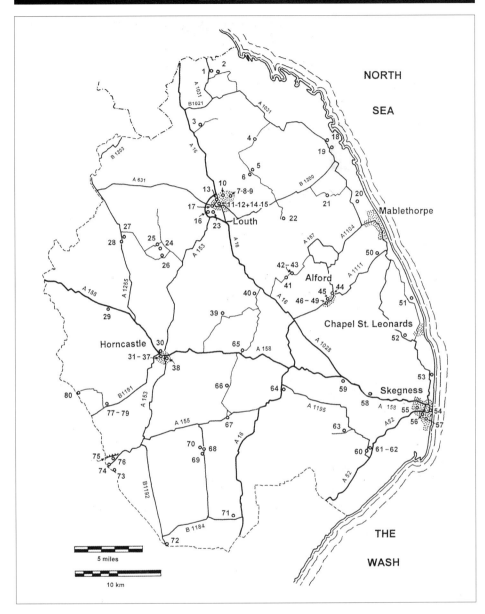

NORTH

SEA

Mablethorpe

Louth

Alford

Chapel St. Leonards

Horncastle

Skegness

THE

WASH

5 miles

10 km

This large district occupies the eastern half of central Lincolnshire, and includes nearly all of the sea coast from the Wash to the Humber.    At the centre of East Lindsey are the Lincolnshire Wolds, encircled by the lower-lying lands of the Coastal Marsh, the Fens, and the valleys of the Witham and the Ancholme.    The Wolds are one of the highest areas of land in eastern England and they have a range of radar and radio masts and associated structures.    The area includes

**14**

the small market towns of Louth, Horncastle and Alford as well as numerous villages. At New Bolingbroke are the remains of an unsuccessfull attempt to create a new planned town in the 1820s, by contrast to the successful new town at Woodhall Spa. The district has remains of railways, a few turnpike tollhouses, the former Louth and Horncastle canals, water mills, preserved windmills at Alford, Burgh-le-Marsh and Sibsey, land drainage, Victorian planned farms and the development of seaside resorts at Skegness and elsewhere.

EL1: Beam Station, Tetney – CJL

EL4: Navigation Warehouse, Austen Fen, Grainthorpe – KR

## EL1 BEAM STATION, TETNEY
*East of A1031 Grimsby Road, about ½ mile from village centre.*
TA 314028
*Access: Can be viewed from public road*
Transmitter buildings built by Marconi for the Post Office Imperial Wireless Scheme in 1927. Transmitted to India and Australia using the HF "Beam" system. The station closed in 1939 but guy rope anchorages for the aerial towers can still be seen in the adjacent field. The receiving station was at Burgh le Marsh.

## EL2 TETNEY OIL TERMINAL
*Minor road between Tetney and Tetney Lock*
TA 331021
*Access: can be viewed from a public road*
This deep water crude oil importing terminal was built by Conoco in the early 1970s. A monobuoy, the first to be installed in British waters, is anchored in position about three miles (4.8km) offshore. Tankers moor alongside and discharge their cargoes of crude oil through a 36inch (1.1m) pipeline to the eight two-million-barrel-capacity storage tanks on shore. From here the oil transfers to the refinery at South Killingholme through a 14 mile (23km) buried pipeline.

## EL3 LUDBOROUGH RAILWAY MUSEUM
*Fulstow Road, Ludborough*
TF 308961
*Open occasional Sundays throughout the year; admission charge; tea room. Phone: 01507 363881. Website* www.louthnet.com
The recently established Lincolnshire Wolds Railway operates a small section of the East Lincolnshire Railway (Grimsby to Boston) which opened in 1848 and closed in 1970. Local enthusiasts run steam trains and maintain various rolling stock over a short stretch of line.

## EL4 NAVIGATION WAREHOUSE, AUSTEN FEN, GRAINTHORPE
*Fen Road, Grainthorpe, Louth*
TF 369946
*Can be viewed from a public road*
An attractive late C18 three-storey brick warehouse on the bank of the Louth Navigation in the middle of the Marsh. It served the commercial needs of the local communities in the C19. This lower section of the navigation, where it crossed the Marsh, was opened in 1767.

## EL5 ALVINGHAM WATERMILL

*Church Lane, Alvingham*
TF 365913
*Access: can be viewed from public road; visits by*
*private arrangement with the owners (01507 327544)*
Watermill hereabouts since C12. Present brick
house and adjacent lower storey of mill built in
1770s, contemporary with the nearby Louth
Navigation. The mill was extended and upper
storey added c1820s when the machinery was
updated. Worked by the Betts family until the
1960s; present owners lovingly restored the mill
to full operation. Two pairs of Peak stones
overdriven by 11ft (3.35m) iron breast shot
wheel. Its water comes from the R Lud via a
culvert under the Louth Navigation in a 1.5m
(5ft) diameter brick tunnel or inverted siphon
60m (197ft) long and returns to the Lud via
another culvert under the canal.

**16**
EL6 – Alvingham Lock – KR

## EL6 ALVINGHAM LOCK; WILLOWS LOCK, ALVINGHAM; CARROTTS LOCK, KEDDINGTON; TICKLEPENNY LOCK, KEDDINGTON; AND KEDDINGTON LOCK

*Lock Road, Alvingham; minor roads in and around*
*Keddington*
Alvingham Lock - TF 365908; Willows Lock - TF
356902; Carrotts Lock - TF 352895; Ticklepenny Lock
- TF 351889; Keddington Lock - TF 345886
*Access: Alvingham Lock is the most complete and*
*can be readily viewed from a public road. Willows*
*Lock is also adjacent to a road bridge. The others can*
*be seen from the public footpath which follows the S*
*and E bank for the full length of the navigation.*
These are five of the six upper locks on the
Louth Navigation, which was designed by John
Grundy and constructed between 1767 and
1770. The locks are timber floored and scal-
loped in plan with four segmental brick arches
on each side. Only one lock elsewhere in the
UK was built to this design, this also in Lincolnshire, between Sibsey and Stickney. The
Louth Navigation was abandoned in 1924 but
a local society is working to preserve what remains.

## EL7 LOUTH RIVERHEAD CANAL BASIN

*Riverhead and Commercial Road, Louth*
TF 337879
*Alongside public roads.*
The Louth Navigation was surveyed by John
Grundy, engineer of Spalding, in 1756 and

opened to this basin from Tetney Haven 11.5 miles to the north in 1770. Several substantial warehouses (some converted to dwellings) and workers' houses remain, as well as the Woolpack Inn.

### EL8 WATERMILLS, LOUTH
*Hubbard's Hills; Westgate; Bridge Street; James Street; Ramsgate Road; Thames Street*
TF 318869; TF 321873; TF 325875; TF 332877; TF 336879; TF 337879.
*All can be viewed from public roads*
There are six remaining mill structures in the town. The mill in James Street provided water power for a carpet factory and Baines' Mill on Thames Street ground corn. See EL9, 14, 16 and 17 for the others.

### EL9 CROWN MILL, LOUTH
*Ramsgate Road*
TF 336879
*Can be viewed from public road*
This four-storey watermill was built in 1716 and enlarged in the mid- to late- C19. At one time it was known as Bryan Hall's Mill. It ground corn for flour and in later years for animal food. Water power via a Gilkes turbine was later supplemented including gas engine and reciprocating oil engine. Now converted to private dwellings and all machinery removed.

### EL10 LOUTH RAILWAY STATION
*Station Approach, off Ramsgate Road*
TF 333879
*Can be viewed from public road*
The GNR's East Lincolnshire Line opened in 1848 and closed in 1970. The brick station building, with its fine porte-cochere, was erected in 1854 in neo-Jacobean style. It has Grade II* listing and now provides private residential accommodation.

### EL11 MARKET HALL, LOUTH
North of Market Place
TF 328874
*Access: Open for trading*
Built by Louth Corporation in 1866-67 at a cost of £7,000. Designed by Rogers and Marsden, the front in red brick and Welsh slate is in Venetian Gothic style with a prominent clock tower. To the rear is an arched cast iron and glass hall, of seven bays, resembling a London railway terminus.

EL11: Market Hall, Louth – KR

### EL12 LOUTH MUSEUM
4 Broadbank
TF 328875
*Summer only; admission charge. Phone: 01507 601211*
A small privately run museum with information about, and artefacts from, local industries.

### EL13 COUNTY HOSPITAL (WORKHOUSE), LOUTH
*High Holme Road*
TF 326877
*Access: houses the local NHS hospital and the site is accessible to the public.*
One of George Gilbert Scott's many workhouses, constructed in 1837 at a cost of £8,000. The single-storey block at the front of the site was the entrance and reception area. Its centre archway gave access for horse-drawn vehicles to the three-story building behind which housed most of the 300 paupers. Outbuildings and a 2-storey infirmary to the rear were demolished when the hospital was established on the site.

EL13: County Hospital, Louth – KR

## EL14 BRIDGE STREET MILL, LOUTH

*Bridge Street*
*TF 325875*
*Access: View from Bridge Street*
Adjacent to the bridge over the R Lud, attractive four floored brick building in Flemish Bond sometimes called St Mary's Mill. Plaque commemorates French immigrant builder "Frans Julien, engineer, 1755". Position of two former waterwheels (once enclosed) can be seen on exterior basement wall. Note tablet on front wall near parapet of bridge inscribed "Flood Level May 29th 1920". All machinery long removed. Building restored by Louth Civic Trust, now a private house.

## EL15 CROWTREE HOSPITAL, LOUTH

*Crow Tree Lane*
*TF 324871*
*Access: can be viewed from the public road*
Built of contrasting coloured brick in flamboyant Victorian Gothic style in 1873 at a cost of £2,000. It has recently been remodelled to provide teaching accommodation for the adjacent King Edward VI School.

## EL16 WESTGATE MILL, LOUTH

*Westgate Road*
*TF 321873*
*Access: View from Westgate Road*
**18** Ancient watermill site. Present structure used as papermill between 1780s and 1840s. Re-

verted to cornmilling c1844. Cast iron axle and hub of former 18ft (5.5m) dia. waterwheel survive in wheel pit. Now converted to private dwelling.

## EL17 HUBBARD'S HILL MILL, LOUTH

*Crowtree Lane, west of Louth centre*
*TF 318869*
*Access: View from public road*
Early C19 lime washed brick building. Sited at the lower end of the delightful Hubbard's Hill Park. Former corn mill with bake house attached. Composite breast shot 16ft (4.9m) dia. waterwheel and sluice survive, all other machinery removed. Now a private house.

## EL18 NEW INN, SALTFLEET

*On the main road through the village, A1031*
*TF 454938*
*Access: still operates as a public house with usual opening hours*
A C17 building with C18 extensions created to meet the demand for sea bathing. A branch of the Louth turnpike provided a good road connection for visitors. The view of the ocean and direct access to the shore were lost in 1854 when the salt marsh frontage was enclosed.

EL19: Tidal Outfall Sluice, Saltfleet – KR

## EL19 TIDAL OUTFALL SLUICE, SALTFLEET

*At southern end of main village street (A1031)*
TF 457934
*Access: Alongside public road; can be viewed from drain bank*
Originally constructed in 1650 to control water levels in the South and North Creeks leading to Saltfleet Haven. Saltfleet was a significant port in the medieval period. There is a row of C19 coastguard cottages across the road.

EL21: Gayton Drainage Engine, Theddlethorpe All Saints – KR

EL23: Turnpike Tollhouse, Hallington – KR

## EL20 THEDDLETHORPE GAS TERMINAL

*On A1031 three miles north of Mablethorpe*
TF 487873
*Access: can be viewed from public road*
This modern complex, looking very similar to an oil refinery, was built 1971-72 where the natural gas from the North Sea comes ashore and from where it is distributed inland by pipeline.

## EL21 GAYTON DRAINAGE ENGINE, THEDDLETHORPE ALL SAINTS

*Minor road from Theddlethorpe St Helen to Saltfleetby St Peter*
TF 457880
*Occasional weekend opening; admission charge.*
*Phone: 01754 890209*
The Gayton Engine Pumping Station was built in 1850 to pump water from marshy farmland into the R Great Eau. The original steam engine was replaced by a Petter 2-stroke ex-marine diesel powering a 27 inch (68.6cm) pump in 1945. This was later replaced by an electric pumping station on the Great Eau closer to the sea. The diesel engine and pump are still operated on "open days".

## EL22 LITTLE CARLTON WATERMILL

*Beside road to Great Carlton*
TF 401854
*Access: View from public road*
Three storied brick mill with pantiled roof; wall plaque records erection in 1820. Still contains much of machinery, which was powered by an iron breast shot wheel by Saunderson of Louth. Large brick granary store to the rear adjacent to R Great Eau. Contemporary attractive mill house and rare detached bake house with flash oven on same site.

## EL23 TURNPIKE TOLLHOUSE, HALLINGTON

*On A153, 1 mile south-west of Louth town centre.*
TF 319860
*A private house viewable from the public road*
A brick and slate building at the Hallington junction on the Horncastle road close to the edge of Louth. The road was turnpiked in 1770. The building has original windows and a door set diagonally in the corner for vision towards Louth.

## EL24 RAILWAY TUNNEL, WITHCALL

*Both entrances about 0.5 miles from minor road from Louth to Donington on Bain*
TF 262820 and TF 268827

EL25: Stenigot Radar Tower – CJL

*On private agricultural land; only accessible with permission*
On Lincoln and Louth Railway through the Wolds. This section of line opened 1876 and closed to passengers 1951 and goods traffic in 1956. The length of the tunnel is 888m (971yds). From the Louth direction the steep climb both up to and inside the tunnel caused traction problems in wet conditions.

### EL25 STENIGOT RADAR TOWER
*Adjacent to Hallington to Donington-on-Bain road*
TF 257825
*Can be viewed from public road*
360ft (110m) high steel lattice tower, the only survivor of four transmitter towers forming part of RAF Stenigot Chain Home Radar Station. Chain Home was the world's first air defence radar system. Some buildings survive. Listed.

### EL26 TOP FARM, HOME FARM, MOSES FARM AND MANOR FARM, STENIGOT
*4 miles south-west of Louth.*
TF 262813, TF 258812, TF 250811, TF 247819
*Access: visible from the public road; direct access only with permission*
**20** Home Farm of 1910 is the last of the county's farmsteads to be built in the High Victorian farm

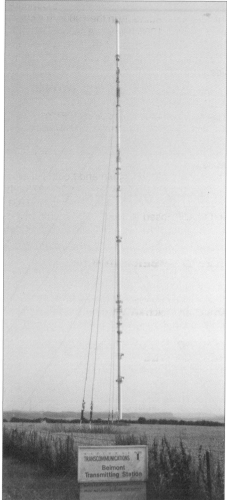

EL27: Belmont Television Mast – KR

tradition. The Stenigot Estate was also innovative in its very early use of reinforced concrete for its new buildings, as at Home, Moses and Manor Farms; also the water tower at Stenigot Wold (TF 256826).

### EL27 BELMONT TELEVISION MAST, SOUTH WILLINGHAM
*Alongside B1225 (Caistor High Street) 10 miles north of Horncastle.*
TF 218838
*Access: can be viewed from public road*

At the time of its construction for the Independent Television Authority in the 1960s this structure (385m or 1263ft) was the second tallest in Europe. The diameter of the hollow steel tubular mast is 2.7m (9ft) and there is a lift inside.

### EL28 RAILWAY TUNNEL, SOUTH WILLINGHAM

*A few hundred metres either side of the B1225 (Caistor High Street) about 9 miles north of Horncastle*
TF 215827 and TF 211830
*On private agricultural land; only accessible with permission*

This section of the Lincoln and Louth Railway through the Wolds was opened in 1875. It ceased to provide a passenger service in 1951 and finally closed in 1956. The length of the tunnel through the ridge of Caistor High Street is 512m (560yds).

### EL29 BAUMBER BRICK KILN

*Alongside A158 1½ miles west of Baumber*
TF 195752
*Access: by arrangement with the owner*
An arched scotch kiln with abutting firing sheds. Well restored by owner in 1980s.

### EL30 NORTH CANAL BASIN, HORNCASTLE

*Watermill Road, north of Market Place*
TF 259698
*Access: View from public road*

The northern basin of the Horncastle Navigation, developed from the R Bain in 1802, is badly silted but still retains one wall following the redevelopment of the area in the late 1990s. There are also remains of Stevenson's watermill at the northern end of the basin and several warehouses in the adjacent streets. The C19 flour mill was originally water driven and was later converted to steam. Although all of the original windows have either been blocked up or replaced the building is still in use and the position of the water wheel may be seen on the side.

### EL31 WOOL WAREHOUSE, HORNCASTLE

*Bridge Street*
TF 257697
*Access: can be viewed from public road*
This 1864 building is now an antiques shop. Although there have been some changes on the outside, internally little has changed and

EL29: Brick Kiln, Baumber – KR

EL30: Flour Mill, North Basin of Canal, Horncastle – JT

EL31: Wool Warehouse, Horncastle – JT

some of the original hoist machinery still survives.

### EL32 CANAL WAREHOUSES, HORNCASTLE

*Behind premises in Bridge Street and West Street*
TF 255695
*Along public roads. Two are currently antique furniture showrooms.*
There used to be several warehouses along **21**

EL33: Harrison's Grain Warehouse, Horncastle – JT

EL35: Warehouse, Banks Street, Horncastle – KR

West Street and Bridge Street backing onto the Bain branch of the Navigation, including one at the western end with two houses and a warehouse under the same roof, but now only a few of the smaller ones survive.

### EL33 HORNCASTLE RAILWAY STATION
*Off Langton Hill*
TF 255694
*Can be seen from public road*
This was the terminus of the branch line opened in 1855, closed to passengers in 1955 and for goods in 1971. Close by is the former grain warehouse of Harrison & Son. This 3-storey brick building dating from the C19 retains hoists and canopy. In 2003 it had been sold for re-development into flats.

### EL34 SOUTHERN CANAL BASIN, HORNCASTLE
*Wharf Road and Jubilee Way*
TF 259695
*Alongside public road*
Almost all trace of the South Basin disappeared when a new concrete course was constructed after the 1960s flood and the A158 relief road was created in 1977.

### EL35 WAREHOUSE, HORNCASTLE
*Banks Street*
TF 261696
*In a public street*
This ornate warehouse of 1890 was probably built for Stephen Pollexfen who had moved into 8 Banks Street sometime before 1900 and is

EL36 – Hopton Ironworks, Horncastle – JT

described as a corn, oil cake and seed merchant. It was later used as a depot and showroom by Ward, Agricultural Engineers.

### EL36 WILLIAM ASHTON'S HOPTON IRONWORKS, HORNCASTLE

*The Wong*
TF 260693
*Access: alongside street and in occupation of antique business*
The only remaining part of the former iron works (1873) has been restored and is now an antiques shop.

### EL37 THOMAS TUPHOLME'S UNION IRON FOUNDRY, HORNCASTLE

*Foundry Street*
TF 263693
*Access: can be viewed from public road*
Although most of the buildings of this C19 foundry remain, they have been very much altered over the years.

### EL38 HOLMES WINDMILL, HORNCASTLE

*Spilsby Road*
TF 266696
*Access: can be viewed from public road*
Sole survivor of at least five windmills formerly in the town, three of them multi-sailed. Built in 1843 as a seven storied tower mill with five patent sails driving four pairs of stones. Top fourteen feet removed in the late 1970s. Worked by wind until 1916 and auxiliary power until the 1940s. Restoration contemplated by present owner.

### EL39 WATERMILL, TETFORD

*5 miles north-east of Horncastle.*
TF 332745
*Access: Can be seen from road.*
The oldest parts of the watermill date from the C17, though the present bakehouse and miller's house are thought to be C18, and the wheel mid-C19. Milling finished after severe floods in 1947 and six years later the mill pond was filled in.

### EL40 KETSBY WATERMILL, SOUTH ORMSBY

*Minor road from Swaby to South Ormsby*
TF 369767
*Can be viewed from public road*
This privately preserved mill of c1864 has a breast-shot wheel, one of the last iron water wheels to turn in Lincolnshire.

EL40: Ketsby Watermill,
South Ormsby – JAS

**23**

EL41: Belleau Dovecote – KR

EL43: Railway Goods Shed, Aby – KR

## EL41 BELLEAU DOVECOTE

*Close to minor road past Belleau church*
TF 402785
*Access: can be viewed from public road; farm track alongside building expected to become a bridleway.*
An early C16 dovecote associated with Belleau Manor. It is an octagonal single-storey structure in red brick with slate roof and boarded lantern. Internally there are square brick nesting boxes. It has Grade II* listing.

**24**
EL44: Hoyle's Mill, Alford – KR

## EL42 CLAYTHORPE WATERMILL, ABY

*On minor road from Aby to Authorpe ½ mile north of Aby village*
TF 414790
*Open daily March to October; admission charge; tea room.  Phone: 01507 450687; website*
*www.claythorpewatermill.co.uk*
This 3-storey brick corn mill c1820 was the last watermill working regularly in Lincolnshire, but the water power has not been used since 1977. The waterwheel was replaced by an Empire turbine after a fire in 1903.

## EL43 RAILWAY GOODS SHED, ABY

*Close to minor road from Aby to Authorpe*
TF 412791
*On private land; can be viewed from public road*
An intact and unmodified brick goods shed on the site of the former Aby Station on GNR's East Lincolnshire line.  Part of one platform and the station house also remain.

## EL44 HOYLE'S WINDMILL, ALFORD

*East Street, Alford*
TF 457766
*Access: Open all year (dates and times vary); admission charge; tea room.   Phone 01507 462136.*
*enquiries@fivesailed.co.uk*
A 5-sail brick tower corn mill dating from 1837. It was built by Sam Oxley, an Alford millwright, with later ironwork and gearing from Tuxfords of Boston.  Apart from minor interruptions the mill has worked continuously since then.   A major improvement project in 2000 enhanced the mill together with adjacent miller's house, bakery, sail shed and engine house.

## EL45 MANOR HOUSE FOLK MUSEUM , ALFORD

*West Street*
TF 453760
*Access: Open all year (times vary); admission charge; tea room.  Phone: 01507 462143*
A private museum in a superb thatched building.  Space is given to material about local industries and a small collection of farm machinery.

## EL46 MILLWRIGHT'S WORKSHOP, ALFORD

*Parsons Lane*
TF 451758
*Access: View from public road or owners R Thompson & Son (01507 462292)*
Premises continually occupied by Alford millwrights since at least early C19, first by

EL48: Alford Railway Station – KR

Oxley's then Wheatcroft. Robert Thompson, a Yorkshire born millwright, took over the premises in 1877. Brick and pantiled workshop contains woodworking machinery, pattern loft and small foundry. Adjacent buildings and yard are an Aladdin's Cave of spare parts for traditional mills. Home made travelling saw bench for sawing out sail timbers etc. was formerly driven by an old tractor. A rare survival of a working traditional millwright/engineer's premises.

## EL47 FORMER TRAMWAY DEPOT, ALFORD
*West Street*
TF 446754
*Access: Can be viewed from public road*
Across the road from the former Railway Station is the unpretentious depot of the Alford and Sutton Tramway, opened 1884 and closed 1889 because of the irresistible competition of the Willoughby to Sutton railway line. It is now used as a bus garage.

## EL48 ALFORD RAILWAY STATION
*Beechings Way, off West Street*
TF 446754
*Access: Can be viewed from public road*
A fine example of a small town station, opened in 1848 for the East Lincolnshire Railway and closed by Beeching cuts in 1970.

## EL49 TURNPIKE TOLLHOUSE, ALFORD
*Station Road*
TF 445754
*Access: Private house, but can be viewed from public road*
Built in 1765 for the Alford branch of the Louth to Boston turnpike road. It was moved to its current position 300yds to the west of the railway level crossing when the railway was built in 1848.

## EL50 BRICKWORKS, SUTTON ON SEA
Sutton Ings
TF 503807
*Access: brick yard now caravan site; permission from owners at site office*
Good example of small local brick yard, once common along Lincolnshire coast and R Humber. Clay pits and complete former Scotch kiln. Rare brick towered drainage pump, last to survive in the county. The 12ft (3.7m) high tower still contains remains of pump gear and cranked windshaft which once carried four hand clothed sails.

## EL51 ANDERBY DRAINAGE ENGINE
Gowts Bridge, Anderby Creek
TF 546759
*Building close to public road. Occasional public open days. Phone: 01754 871594 or 01754 872599*
A diesel powered pumping station that operated for nearly 50 years. It was preserved by the Alford Drainage Board when the new electrically operated pumping station was opened on the adjoining site in 1992. The building also houses a small museum which includes land drainage equipment.

## EL52 WINDPUMP, HOGSTHORPE
*Hill View fishing Lakes, ¼ mile east of Hogsthorpe, beside road to Ingoldmells.*
TF 538715
*Access: View from road*
An example of the windpumps once to be found on numerous Lincolnshire farms. Made by Godwins of Gloucester. This 18-sail pump with "Hercules" wind engine moved here from Hogsthorpe Barracks and re-erected as fully functional pump in 1980s.

## EL53 BUTLIN'S FIRST CHALET, INGOLDMELLS
*In holiday camp, 2 miles north of Skegness.*
TF 573672
*Access: Charge for admission to holiday camp.*
Billy Butlin opened the first holiday camp in Britain at Ingoldmells at Easter 1936. Most of the early chalets, which were timber-framed with an infill of asbestos panels, have been replaced but one still survives.

## EL54 SKEGNESS PIER
*Grand Parade/North Parade.*
TF 573634
*Access: Remains can be viewed from beach and promenade.*
The pier, built in 1881, was the fourth longest

in England at 1843 feet (562m). From the end of the pier, the site of a pavilion and concert hall, boat trips were run around the Wash and to Hunstanton. Storms destroyed much of the seaward end (except the large pier head itself) on the night of 11th/12th January 1978.

### EL55 CHURCH FARM MUSEUM, SKEGNESS

*Church Road South*
TF 558636
*Open daily in summer season; admission charge; tea room. Phone: 01754 766658*
A group of small-scale traditional farm buildings dating from the 1760s with C19 additions. Lincolnshire buildings from elsewhere, including a mud-and-stud cottage and a timber-framed barn, have been transferred to the site.

Local agricultural implements are on display and there are regular demonstrations of farming and rural craft activities.

### EL56 SKEGNESS RAILWAY STATION

*Junction of Roman Bank, Wainfleet Road and Richmond Drive*
TF 562631
*Access: still operating*
Opened in 1873 with a single line connection to Firsby on the East Lincolnshire line, within 10 years as many as 20,000 day trippers arrived on August Bank Holiday. The line was doubled in 1900 and the station was rebuilt in 1936.

EL56: Skegness
Railway Station – KR

## EL57 SKEGNESS, PLANNED RESORT

*The area enclosed by Roman Bank, Lumley Road, Grand Parade and Scarbrough Avenue*
TF 563633
*Access: can be viewed from public streets*

A grand plan for a new town was drawn up in the 1870s by the agent of the Earl of Scarbrough, the principal landowner at a time when Skegness was a village with a population of about 500. The scheme included a new sea wall, a geometric plan of wide tree-lined avenues, houses in standard styles, pleasure grounds, sea water baths and a theatre.

## EL58 DOBSON'S WINDMILL, BURGH LE MARSH

*Skegness Road.*
TF 503649
*Access : open most Sundays 2-5pm, Easter to October, phone: 01754 766658.*

A 5-storey, 5-sailed brick tower mill built c1813 by Sam Oxley of Alford, together with a range of outbuildings. It retains a full range of machinery and equipment, including 3 pairs of stones, and has unusual left-handed sails (i.e. they rotate clockwise). It worked commercially until 1964 and, under the ownership of the County Council, has occasionally operated since.

## EL59 GUNBY HALL DOVECOTE

*In the gardens of Gunby Hall, 7 miles west of Skegness off A158.*
TF 467669
*Access: National Trust property, open April to September, Weds & Thurs afternoons and by appointment.*

A square, red brick building constructed as a garden feature in the early C18. The hall is dated 1700. The original framework and ladder (potence) for gaining access to the pigeon holes are still in place. Grade II listed.

## EL60 SALEM BRIDGE BREWERY, WAINFLEET ALL SAINTS

*Main street near town centre.*
TF 495587
*Access: Visitor centre open 11.30 to 3.30 every day. Food and drink.*

Lincolnshire's oldest independent brewery was established by George Bateman in 1874 and is still operated by the same family. The site includes the tower of a windmill as well as a collection of brewing equipment and other historical exhibits.

## EL61 BARKHAM STREET, WAINFLEET ALL SAINTS

*150 yards north of Market Place.*
TF 498591
*Access: a public street.*

Sydney Smirke, eminent Victorian architect, was commissioned by Bethlem Hospital, a London-based charity, to design houses for their land in the centre of Wainfleet in 1847. The result was this pair of long matching terraces of 3-storey brick houses, straight out of a London design book. Their appearance in a small Lincolnshire market town is both surprising and incongruous.

**27**

EL58: Dobson's Mill, Burgh le Marsh – KR

EL61: Barkham Street, Wainfleet All Saints – NRW

## EL62 MAGDALEN MUSEUM, WAINFLEET ALL SAINTS

*St John Street.*
TF 498587
*Open in Summer daily except Monday and Wednesday; admission charge; tea room. Phone: 01754 880343*
A fine medieval brick building (former school) dating from 1484 which houses the public library and a small first-floor museum with information on local industries.

## EL63 THORPE CULVERT, THORPE ST PETER

*Minor road across Steeping River 3 miles north-west of Wainfleet.*
TF 469607
*Access: can be viewed from public road.*
Designed by John Rennie, c1820. Three parallel 5ft 7in (1.7m) oval brick tunnels 140ft (42.7m) long under the Steeping River. Built to connect the "5000 acres" east of the Steeping River to the East Fen drainage system.

## EL64 RAILWAY GOODS WAREHOUSE, SPILSBY

*Boston Road.*
TF 401658
*Access: Visible from public road.*
Surviving building of terminus of 4.5 mile long Spilsby and Firsby Railway, opened 1st May 1868 and operated by the GNR. The branch line closed to passengers on 11th September 1939 and to freight traffic in 1958, and this building was used for many years by Sinclairs of Boston as a seed, animal feed and fertilizer warehouse.

## EL65 STOCKWITH WATERMILL, HAGWORTHINGHAM

*Harrington Road.*
TF 358705
*Open all year; tea room. Phone: 01507 588221.*
Delightful setting, reputedly "Phillips Farm" from Tennyson's poem "The Brook". Fine external wood and iron waterwheel with wooden axle powered by the R Lymm. For two centuries until 1919 it ground corn for the nearby Harrington Hall estate. Later it powered an electricity generator and was in regular use until 1960. All internal machinery now removed.

## EL66 MODEL FARM, HAREBY, OLD BOLINGBROKE

*At minor road junction 1 mile WNW of Old Bolingbroke.*
TF 336657
*Alongside public road.*
A planned farmstead constructed for Sir J. J. Smith in a single phase c1850. Like several other new tenanted farmsteads in the county of the Victorian High Farming period, it was designed in plain but robust manner to reflect the best mixed farming practice of the age. The barn was designed for portable steam power, an innovation in the 1850s. The stables are in a detached block across the road.

## EL67 AIRCRAFT CONTROL TOWER, EAST KIRKBY

*Off the A155 east of the village centre*
TF 337625
*Open Monday to Saturday throughout the year; admission charge; tea room. Phone: 01790 763207. Website www.lincsaviation.co.uk*

EL69: Crescent, New Bolingbroke – SJW

The original control tower and an Avro Lancaster Bomber (mobile, but not airworthy) are highlights of the Lincolnshire Aviation Heritage Centre based on this 1940s airfield site. There is a large visitor centre with displays and exhibitions of photographs.

### EL68 NAVIGATION BASIN, NEW BOLINGBROKE
*Off main road B1183, ¼ mile north of church.*
TF 308582
*Access: can be viewed from public road.*
The Medlam Drain provides a navigable north-south route from Revesby to Frithville and on to Boston. A half-mile branch leads to the settlement of New Bolingbroke, established as an intended industrial market town in the middle of the reclaimed fens in the 1820s. John Parkinson, the progenitor of the unsuccessful scheme, built a factory at the waterside basin with the aim of producing crepes and bombazines.

### EL69 MARKET HOUSE, NEW BOLINGBROKE
*Main Road.*
TF 308579
*Alongside public road.*
This building still remains in the intended market square, though the ground floor arches are now bricked up. On the other side of the main road is a crescent of shops and houses. The rows of workers' cottages, built in typical Victorian terraces along the roadside, have gaps for cross streets which were never constructed.

EL70: Globe Foundry,
New Bolingbroke – KH

### EL70 GLOBE FOUNDRY, NEW BOLINGBROKE
*Main road, north of village centre.*
TF 307586
*Occupied but can be viewed from the public road.*
This also dates from the original foundation of the settlement and produced agricultural machinery until 2002. The site also includes a redundant windmill, minus cap, sails and machinery.

### EL71 SIBSEY TRADER WINDMILL
*Frithville Road B1184, ½ mile west of A16.*
TF 344510
*Open every weekend, Bank Holiday and Tuesday in summer; Saturdays rest of year (English Heritage); adm. charge. (01205) 460647;*
www.sibsey.fsnet.co.uk
This six-sail mill built by John Saunderson of Louth in 1877 was one of the last tower mills to be erected in Lincolnshire. It worked commercially until 1954 (latterly with only 4-sails). Open to the public since 1981; a further resto- **29**

EL71: Sibsey Trader Windmill – KR

ration project was completed in 2002. The only other surviving 6-sailed mill is at Waltham (NE18).

## For Cowbridge see BN7 to BN9, Fishtoft in Boston District

### EL72 LANGRICK BRIDGE

*Crossing of the R Witham by the B1192 4 miles NW of Boston.*
TF 265478
*Public road.*

The steel bow girder bridge over the R Witham was built in 1908 at the joint expense of the GNR (which controlled the navigation) and the local authorities on either bank. It replaced a long established ferry.

### EL73 DOGDYKE PUMPING STATION, TATTERSHALL

*Aproach through Bridge Farm yard on south side of A153, 500 yards east of Tattershall Bridge.*
TF 206558
*Open 1st Sunday in each month from Easter to October 2pm – 5pm. Phone: 01526 342352.*

Fen drainage began on this site in 1796 with a windpump operated by a 30ft (9.1m) sail driving a 16ft (4.9m) diameter waterwheel to lift water from the Mill Drain to the R Witham. In 1855 a 16hp steam engine with a 12ft 6in (3.7m) beam was installed. This drove a 24ft (7.3m) scoop which drained 1500 acres (625 Ha). In 1940 the chimney was demolished as it was a hazard to military flying and a Ruston diesel engine and pump installed. The steam engine has now been restored and is in steam on Open Days.

### EL74 TATTERSHALL BRIDGE

*Next to modern bridge over R Witham, 1½ miles SE of village.*
TF 196562
*Access: can be viewed from public road.*

This red brick bridge, probably by John Rennie, was built in haste about 1815 to replace an earlier bridge of c1795 which collapsed when the river was being dredged. It had stone copings and iron railings of 1920 that were removed in 1977. It was superseded by a new bridge alongside in 1991/92.

### EL75 TATTERSHALL CANAL

*Main village street (A153) to R Witham WSW.*
TF 194571 to TF 213577
*Access: can be viewed from public road.*

This one mile (1.6km) canal with a single lock was constructed from the R Witham to the village centre by John Gibson (and consequently

EL72: Langrick Bridge – KR

back projection (still in use) and deck chairs as front row seats (replaced in 1953).

## EL78 SPA BATHS, WOODHALL SPA

*Spa Road, ¼ mile NE of village centre.*
TF 196636
*Access: Exterior can be viewed from public road.*

A scheme to sink a coal mine in the 1820s foundered, but water from the abandoned shaft was exceptionally high in mineral salts. Thus in 1838 the first pump room and bath house were built and the spa resort founded. Significant alterations and additions took place in the period 1890-1910. The buildings over the spa well collapsed in 1983 and schemes to resurrect the spa have so far foundered.

## EL79 COTTAGE MUSEUM, WOODHALL SPA

*Iddesleigh Road, off east end of Broadway.*
TF 196634
*Open daily in summer season.   Phone: 01526 353775.*

A small community museum with information about the development of the spa, the local railway, Kinema, Dambuster Squadron and RAF Connections.

## EL80 STIXWOULD PUMPING STATION

*East bank of R Witham, 1 mile south of village.*
TF 157652
*Access: View from public road along river bank.*

Typical land drainage pumping station of the 1930s still with its original Ruston diesel engined pumps in working order though now used only as backup to modern electric pumps. The nearby railway bridge still has two of its original cast iron beams.

known as the Gibson Cut) in 1786.   It later provided the initial portion for the Horncastle Navigation (1792-1802) that followed the southwards course of the R Bain.   Its junction with the R Witham is now blocked by an embankment, but it is in water for most of its length.

## EL76 TATTERSHALL RAILWAY STATION

*Alongside the A153 ¾ mile SW of village centre.*
TF 203567
*Access: used as an art & craft shop with regular opening hours.*

An imposing pale brick building in the tower style constructed for the GNR in 1848. The line closed on 5th October 1970 but the platforms and many original features remain.

## EL77 KINEMA IN THE WOODS, WOODHALL SPA

*Spa Road ¼ mile NE of village centre.*
TF 195635
*Access: Still in full-time use as a cinema.*

Was originally a sports pavilion probably erected in the 1880s. Conversion to the Pavilion Cinema took place in 1922 and its present name was first used in 1924. Extensions in 1994 created space for a second screen. Among the unusual features of the cinema are

EL77: Kinema in the Woods, Woodhall Spa – KR

The City of Lincoln is located halfway down the western edge of the county in a gap in the limestone ridge and has been an important communications centre since Roman times. It is the county town, a cathedral city and a market town for its surrounding area but did not industrialise until the middle of the C19. It then became home to not one but several major engineering firms which at first specialised in the production of agricultural machinery. In the late C19 they expanded their range of products, and in the First World War with three major firms making aircraft (Robeys, Clayton & Shuttleworth, and Rustons) the city was the largest aircraft production centre in the world. It is perhaps even more famous as the city where the first British tanks were developed by Fosters at their new Wellington Works (demolished in the 1980s). Other industrial remains include items relating to the waterways and railways that passed through the city, and premises using the produce of the surrounding agricultural area or providing goods for local needs. A vestige of its early history is Ellis's mill, the last survivor of a row of several windmills that once extended along the top of the cliff north of the Lincoln gap.

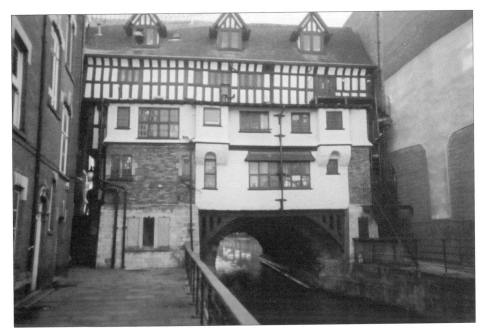
LN1: High Bridge, Lincoln – NRW

### LN1 HIGH BRIDGE
*Where High Street crosses R Witham.*
SK 974712
*Access: Visible from pedestrianised road and footpaths.*
Claimed to be the second oldest masonry arch bridge in Britain, and the only bridge in the country which still has a secular medieval building on it. Dates from c1160 with subsequent extensions (1235, 1540/50, c1902) and alterations, and on west side are shops in a 3-storey C16 timber frame building. River underneath deepened and made navigable 1795. Main A15/A46 road passed over it until 1971.

### LN2 BRUSH WAREHOUSE
*On north bank of Witham east of High Bridge.*
SK 974712
*Access: Can be seen from public footpath along bank.*
This C18 4-storey brick warehouse on the bank of the Witham in the city centre, was converted to offices in 1975 and is unoccupied in 2004.

### LN3 CORN EXCHANGE
*In city centre, just off High Street.*
SK 975710
*Access: Visible from public streets.*
The original classical-style Corn Exchange of 1847 by W.A. Nicholson has been altered several times and had its original roof removed in 2003 during refurbishment of the building. Next to it is the larger Corn Exchange of 1879, which had a covered market, since drastically altered, on the ground floor with the Exchange room on the upper floor. Lincoln Co-op now occupy the upper floor and part of the ground floor.

### LN4 CENTRAL STATION
*In St Mary's Street, at south end of city centre.*
SK 975709
*Access: Railway Station still in use.*
The GNR station of 1848 by John Henry Taylor

LN4: Central Station, Lincoln – NRW

LN6: St Mark's Station, Lincoln – NRW

LN9: Electricity Works, Lincoln – NRW

is a listed building in a Tudor style with a tower to complement that of nearby St Mary le Wigford church.

## LN5 ST MARY'S CONDUIT

*High Street, at south end of city centre, adjacent to level crossing.*
SK 975710
*Access: In public street.*
Originally monastic water supply to Greyfriars, in Broadgate, built from 1535 to 1539 but taken over by Lincoln Corporation and extended in 1539 to St Mary's Conduit and later to St Peter at Gowts Conduit further along High Street. System in use until C19 and briefly during 1905 typhoid epidemic.

## LN6 ST MARK'S STATION

*High Street, ¼ mile south of city centre.*
SK 973707
*Access: now part of pedestrianised shopping centre.*
MR station of 1846 in austere but elegant classical style. The line through the station was closed in 1985 and a decade later the listed building was restored as shops at the centre of a new shopping area. On the opposite side of High Street is an interesting octagonal single storey signal box erected when the original MR station was joined by the MSLR line from the east, crossing the High Street. This signal box is now a fast food outlet.

## LN7 BRAYFORD POOL

*In city centre, west of High Bridge.*
SK 972712
*Access: Public roads and paths on north and east sides.*
This basin has been the centre of inland waterways to the city since Roman times, where the Fossdyke canal joins the R Witham. Until the 1970s Brayford was lined with steam mills

and warehouses but virtually nothing now remains of these. The Pool is now bounded by the University of Lincoln, offices, a hotel, new cinema, restaurants and a pub.

## LN8 GREAT CENTRAL GOODS DEPOT

*On west bank of R Witham, south of Brayford Pool, west of city centre.*
SK 972710
*Access: Visible from public roads.*
Built in 1907 by GCR next to the upper Witham with a loading bay alongside for river craft (filled-in in early 1970s); sold to a builders' merchants in 1967, disused for several years and renovated in 2003/04 to become the Library of the University of Lincoln.

## LN9 ELECTRICITY WORKS, BRAYFORD

*Brayford North, west of the city centre.*
SK 971712
*Access: Can be viewed from public road.*
The original electricity works built by Lincoln Corporation in 1898 was later converted to offices and still stands empty. Behind it is the shell of the large 1913 extension to the works. In 2004 its future is still uncertain.

## LN10 RUSTON BUCYRUS WORKS

*Beevor Street, south-west of city centre.*
SK 965711
*Access: Can be seen from public road.*
Ruston, Proctor & Co. made their first steam excavator in 1874, and since then thousands have been produced on this site. In 1930 Ruston's excavator interests were combined with those of the Bucyrus-Erie Co. of Milwaukee, USA. Production ceased c2000 and most buildings were demolished for a large B & Q Store.

LN12: Chemical Manure Works, Lincoln – NRW

LN15: Le Tall's Crown Mill, Lincoln – NRW

### LN11 FOSSDYKE NAVIGATION
*Extends westwards from Brayford Pool.*
SK 969713 to SK 838780
*Access: Roads and footpaths on north bank.*
This 11-mile long waterway to the Trent at Torksey dates from Roman times. Made navigable again by Henry I in1121 but subsequently deteriorated until restoration in 1740/45 by Richard Ellison. Lock at Torksey (see WL54). At Lincoln there used to be some warehouses on the north side of the canal but none of these remain.

### LN12 CHEMICAL MANURE WORKS
*Roman Wharf, off Carholme Road, mile west of city centre.*
SK 964715
*Access: Can be viewed from public road.*
The mid C19 building where John Jekyll started his chemical business in the 1850s still survives among modern bungalows and houses on the larger site of the extended factory.

### LN13 NEWSUM'S GATEHOUSE
*Carholme Road, mile west of city centre.*
SK 963716
*Access: Visible from public road.*
Newsum was a timber merchant and after 1918 moved to this site where he mass-produced timber prefabricated buildings. An example of the latter, dating to around 1950, is still in use as the gatehouse of the electronics factory (Marconi Applied Technology) which occupies the site today.

### LN14 PYEWIPE TUNNEL
*Beneath Fossdyke Canal at Pyewipe Pumping Station, about 1 mile west of city centre.*
SK 954719
*Access: By public bridleway along north bank of Fossdyke Canal.*
A cast iron drainage tunnel by John Rennie under Fossdyke Canal at Pyewipe. Forty yards (36.6m) long, elliptical section, 16 sq ft area, cast iron segments. (Pumping Station is of the 1930s). Difficult to build because of running sand. Work commenced 1805, completion date unknown but before 1816.

### LN15 LE TALL'S CROWN MILL
*Mill Lane, off High Street, ½ mile south of city centre.*
SK 970703
*Access: Can be viewed from public roads.*
This former steam corn mill incorporates the 9-storey tower of the earlier windmill which was retained to support a water tank. The sails were removed in the 1860s when a beam engine was installed, itself later replaced when the buildings were extended. The water tank was misguidedly removed in the 1980s when the building was converted to apartments.

### LN16 BRICK KILN AND PIT
*West of Cross O'Cliff Hill, alongside the Viking Way Long Distance Footpath.*
SK 975686
*Access: public access to site.*
Remains, including reduced chimney, of the only surviving example of one of the Lincoln area's once numerous brickworks. These remains replaced earlier buildings around 1900 and this works closed about 1907.

LN18: Tram Depot, Lincoln – NRW

## LN17 WALKER'S POTATO CRISP FACTORY

*High Street, about mile south of city centre.*
SK 968686
*Access: Visible from public road.*

Factory built by Smith's in 1938 to make crisps from the potatoes produced on the Nocton Estate several miles south of the city.

## LN18 TRAM DEPOT

*Newark Road, Bracebridge, about mile south of city centre.*
SK 968684
*Access: At side of public street.*

From 1883 Lincoln had a horse tram system running along High Street and Newark Road, from Bracebridge to the city centre, and its depot was here near the southern end of the line. Converted to electric trams in 1905 and closed in 1929. The depot, on the east side of the road, is now a motorcycle accessory shop.

## LN19 SWANPOOL GARDEN SUBURB

*Off Skellingthorpe Road, west of junction with Tritton Road, in south of city.*
SK 951698
*Access: Visible from public roads.*

Colonel Ruston, of the firm of Ruston & Hornsby, provided the impetus for this garden suburb on the edge of Lincoln to house his employees, designed by A.J. Thompson, an associate of Raymond Unwin. Development started in 1919 but due to the depression only four streets of the ambitious scheme were actually built – Almond Avenue, Hartsholme Drive, Westwood Close and Cherry Grove – which are now a Conservation Area.

## LN20 TURNPIKE TOLLHOUSE, CANWICK HILL FOOT

*South-east edge of city, at junction of roads to Branston and Washingborough.*
SK 982700
*Access: visible from public road.*

The Lincoln Turnpike Trust improved the road up Canwick Hill under their 1756 Act by creating a cutting at the top of the hill to relieve the gradient. The toll-house at the hill foot was not built until 1843 when the Trust built Canwick Road and Melville Street as part of a new route from the foot of this hill to Lindum Hill, bypassing the city centre.

LN20: Turnpike Tollhouse, Canwick Hill Foot, Lincoln – NRW

LN21: Part of Perseverance Ironworks, Lincoln – NRW

LN24: Doughty's Oil Mill, Lincoln – NRW

## LN21 PERSEVERANCE IRONWORKS

*Canwick Road, south-east of city centre.*
SK 980704
*Access: Now mainly occupied by Jackson Shipley, Builders Merchants' premises.*
This engineering works was established by Robert Robey in 1854, and became one of the largest in the city. Most of the premises were erected by 1882 and were occupied by Robey's until 1988. Its products included traction engines, steam wagons and colliery winding gear. Many of the large buildings still remain, with new uses.

## LN22 PELHAM BRIDGE

*Crossing the railway lines east of the city centre.*
SK 978708
*Access: still part of the public road.*
Flyover built in 1950s to replace a complex railway level crossing on one of the two main north-south routes through the city centre. Opened by Queen Elizabeth II on 27th June 1958.

## LN23 SINCIL DYKE

*Runs for a mile along eastern side of City Centre, then turns east parallel to R Witham.*
From SK 969696 to SK 983708
*Access: Road, called Sincil Bank, along east bank for some distance.*
Drainage channel probably of medieval origin, with later alterations and improvements. Rennie, Smeaton, Grundy and Jessop all involved at various times. Extended from its original outfall to the R Witham at Stamp End along South Delph to Bardney by John Rennie c1820.

## LN24 DOUGHTY'S OIL MILL

*On south bank of R Witham, east of city centre.*
SK 978710
*Access: Can be viewed from public road.*
This oil seed crushing mill on the bank of the navigable R Witham is a four-storey grey brick classical building of 1863 with a taller block of 1891 to the east. Converted to apartments in the 1990s.

## LN25 SHEAF IRONWORKS

*Waterside South and Melville Street, east of city centre.*
SK 980710
*Access: Can be viewed from public road.*
This was the original premises of Ruston, Procter & Co (formed 1857) which in the C20 became the largest engineering firm in the city, trading as Ruston and Hornsby for about 50 years from 1918. Later occupied by Ruston Gas Turbines, European Gas Turbines, Alsthom and, from 2003, by Siemens.

## LN26 STAMP END IRONWORKS

*On south bank of R Witham, at Stamp End, east of city centre.*
SK 982710
*Access: Can be viewed from public road.*
Clayton & Shuttleworth were one of the largest engineering firms in the world in the 2nd half of the C19. These works were established in 1842 and at its peak the firm also had the Titanic Works, the Abbey Works and the Tower Works in the city as well as its own electricity station. The firm collapsed in 1929 and its premises were split between different owners. Many 1860s buildings survived at Stamp End until 2002/03, and part of the Edwardian offices at the front still remains.

LN26: Part of Stamp End Ironworks, Lincoln – NRW

LN28: Stamp End Railway Bridge, Lincoln – NRW

## LN27 STAMP END LOCK

*South bank of R Witham, ½ mile east of city centre.*
SK 982711
*Access: Can be seen from public road alongside.*

The top lock on the Witham navigation was built in 1770 and rebuilt downstream in 1826 following the extension of Sincil Dyke. The top gates were replaced by a guillotine in 1950 but at the east end there are still lock gates.

## LN28 STAMP END RAILWAY BRIDGE

*Crosses R Witham, ½ mile east of city centre.*
SK 985711
*Access: Visible from roads on both banks.*

Designed by Sir John Fowler, as part of MSLR branch from Grimsby to Lincoln. Main span (1847/48) is a very early (oldest still extant?) example of a Fairbairn wrought iron box girder bridge.

## LN29 TITANIC WORKS AND TITANIC BRIDGE

*On south bank of R Witham at Stamp End, east of city centre.*
SK 985709
*Access: Can be viewed from public road.*

Built by Clayton & Shuttleworth in 1912 and occupied from 1928 until 1989 by Clayton Dewandre Ltd. Took its name from the famous liner which made its only voyage that year, but it is in fact longer and narrower than the ship. A lifting bridge over the Witham was built next to the works, but in the 1980s was fixed in the raised position with steep, ramped approaches.

## LN30 LINDUM ROAD

*East side of city centre.*
SK 978715 to SK 980717
*Access: Still a public road.*

New road built up the hillside with a uniform

LN29: Titanic Ironworks, Lincoln – NRW

gradient in 1786 by Lincoln turnpike trust for north-south traffic to bypass Steep Hill in city centre. Also known as Lindum Hill. In 1843 the trust also built Canwick Road and Melville Street as a new road across fields.

### LN31 BREWERY ATTACHED TO LION AND SNAKE PH

*Bailgate, north of Lincoln Cathedral.*
SK 976719
*Access: Visible from yard of pub.*

One of the few surviving small brewery buildings where a pub brewed its own beer.

### LN32 WESTGATE WATER TOWER

*North of Lincoln Castle, in upper city.*
SK 975721
*Access: Located in small public park.*

Massive stone tower erected 1910/11, engineer N McKecknie Barron, architect Sir Reginald Blomfield and built by Underwood Bros. of Dukinfield. 300,000 gallons capacity, 117 ft (35.7m) high. Designed to resemble a medieval castle keep.

### LN33 MUSEUM OF LINCOLNSHIRE LIFE

*Burton Road, north of Lincoln Castle.*
SK 972721
*Access: Open weekdays and Sunday afternoons; party visits by arrangement. For further information ring 01522 528448.*

The County's major social and industrial history museum run by Lincolnshire County Council. Contains much agricultural and industrial machinery built in Lincolnshire including steam, oil and gas engines. Also a Mark IV World War One tank Flirt II, which was developed in the city. The museum occupies a former Yeomanry Barracks built in 1857.

### LN34 ELLIS'S WINDMILL

*Mill Road, behind Museum of Lincolnshire Life.*
SK 971722
*Access: Open Sunday afternoons and Saturday afternoons in summer; for further information ring 01522 523870 or 528448.*

This hill-top tower windmill of 1798 has 4-sails and only 3-storeys and was restored (from a burnt out shell) in 1977/81 as Lincoln Civic Trust's celebration of Queen Elizabeth II's Silver Jubilee. Now managed by the Museum of Lincolnshire Life next door.

above: LN31: Brewery, Lion and Snake, Lincoln – NRW
right: LN34: Ellis's Mill, Lincoln – NRW

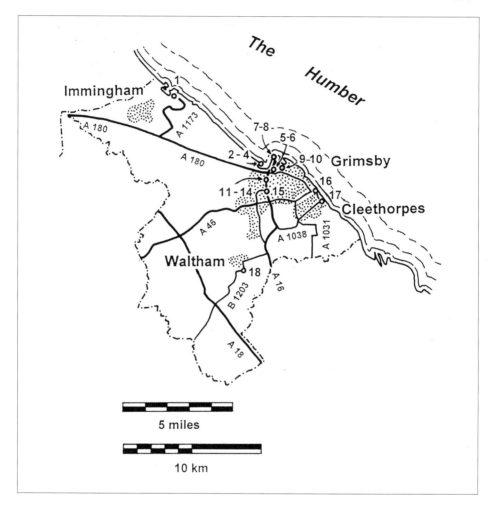

The Humber

Immingham

1

A 180

A 1173

A 180

2 - 4

7-8 -

5-6

9-10 Grimsby

16

11 - 14

15

17

Cleethorpes

A 46

A 1038

A 1031

Waltham

18

B 1203

A 16

A 18

5 miles

10 km

This district contains Grimsby and Cleethorpes which form the largest urban concentration in Lincolnshire.   The ancient town of Grimsby grew, after 1850, into the largest fishing port in the world and expanded into the adjoining village of Cleethorpes which also developed as a Victorian seaside resort.   The fishing industry is now a shadow of its former self but there are still many visible remains of the docks and the related frozen food factories that thrive on processing products brought in by road from elsewhere.   Grimsby Docks were created by the MSLR (later GCR) and the last major addition to the port was the massive dock at Immingham six miles north of Grimsby, closer to deep water. The excessively tall hydraulic tower, redolent of an Italian campanile, on Grimsby's Royal Dock is one of the major industrial monuments of the county.   The District still includes a few small villages in its rural hinterland, and at Waltham is one of the county's restored windmills.

## NE1 IMMINGHAM DOCK

*6 miles north of Grimsby.*
TA 195161
*Access: Restricted public access.*
Built 1906-12 by GCR at cost of £2,600,000 to take larger vessels which could not enter Grimsby Docks. Pioneering use of reinforced concrete in many of the dock structures. The 45-acre basin was at the heart of a 1,000 acre estate and Immingham is now the busiest port on the Humber. Apart from the Dock Office, next to the entrance lock, little remains of the original Edwardian structures.

## NE2 JOHN RENNIE LOCK, GRIMSBY

*Between Alexandra Dock and Union Dock*
TA 272106
*Access: Limited public access*
This lock designed by John Rennie was built in 1798-1800 across the mouth of the original haven to form the first dock at Grimsby after earlier attempts to build a lock here had failed. The lock was closed in 1917 and is now filled in but the stonework is still visible at each end.

## NE3 ALEXANDRA DOCK, GRIMSBY

*At western end of the Dock site.*
TA 267105
*Access: Limited public access.*
Built 1878-80 behind the sea wall at right angles to the former Haven, which was later called the Old Dock and is now part of Alexandra Dock.

## NE4 UNION DOCK, GRIMSBY

*Between Royal and Alexandra Docks.*
TA 273106
*Access: Limited public access.*
Built 1873-74 as a channel to connect Royal Dock to the Old Dock, after which use of Rennie's lock declined. Officially opened 1879, and later widened. Now crossed by a floating footbridge.

## NE5 GRIMSBY DOCK OFFICES

*North end of Victoria Road.*
TA 275106
*Access: View from public road.*
Large building erected at Dock Entrance by MSLR in 1884. Statue of Prince Albert was unveiled on another site in 1879 and moved here c1980.

## NE6 ROYAL DOCK, GRIMSBY

*To the north of Dock Offices*
TA 276110
*Access: Limited public access*
Built by MSLR in 1846-52 on 138 acres of re-claimed foreshore; engineer James Meadows Rendel. The basin covered about 20 acres. All subsequent docks at Grimsby were also built by the railway company. The quay walls were built as a series of brick and stone arches to minimise the pressure on the weak alluvial ground beneath.

NE5: Dock Offices, Grimsby – KR

### NE7 COFFER DAM, GRIMSBY DOCKS
*Along northern-eastern edge of the Docks.*
TA 277113
*Access: Limited public access*
Built 1846-48 to complete sea defences and exclude tide from the site of the Royal Dock, so that the locks and dock basin could be built. Most of the dam was removed in 1854 but the western end can still be seen, clearly showing the method of its construction. Probably the largest coffer dam in Britain when it was built, well over a mile in length and extending over half a mile into the Humber.

NE8: Hydraulic Tower (1851), Grimsby Docks – KR (see also back cover)

### NE8 HYDRAULIC TOWERS, GRIMSBY DOCKS
*At north end of Royal Dock.*
TA 278113
*Access: Limited public access on open days.*
The Royal Dock was the first major dock to use hydraulic power to operate lock gates, cranes, etc. and the great red brick tower, designed by J W Wild and based on the campanile of the Palazzo Pubblico of Siena, was the source of that power. It was not an accumulator tower in the true sense of that term, but a static head of water for the hydraulic mains, consisting of a 33,000 gallon tank into which water was pumped by a steam engine. It is 303ft (92.4m) high and was built in 1851 between the two locks at the seaward end of the Royal Dock. The hydraulic machinery on the Dock was by William Armstrong of Newcastle. Nearby is a 78ft (23.7m) high accumulator tower built in 1892 for a high pressure hydraulic system which replaced the 1851 low pressure installation. The 1851 tower has been given Grade I listed building status and is now used to support aerials and to supply water to wash down the fish pontoon. The 1892 tower was made redundant in 1980 by the installation of an electrically driven oil-hydraulic operation.

### NE9 FISH DOCKS, GRIMSBY
*To the east of the Royal Dock.*
TA 283110
*Access: Limited public access.*
Built in several stages as this industry, previously unknown in Grimsby, expanded: No.1 – 1855-57, extended 1866; No.2 – 1876-77, extended 1897-1900; No.3 – 1934. The fishing industry was destroyed by the Cod Wars with Iceland, but processing fish from other ports, and vegetables etc, continues.

### NE10 ICE FACTORY, GRIMSBY DOCKS
*On west side of Fish Docks.*
TA 278108
*Access: Limited public access.*
This former Ice Factory alongside the Fish Docks in Grimsby was built, in red brick, in 1900-01 and extended in 1907-08. Built for the Great Grimsby Ice Company Ltd., it retains much of the machinery which supplied ice to the trawlers for packing fish. It closed in 1990. It is believed to be the earliest remaining ice factory in the UK and the sole survivor complete with machinery.

NE10: Ice Factory, Grimsby Docks – JAS

NE11: Victoria Flour Mills, Grimsby - KR

### NE11 VICTORIA FLOUR MILLS, GRIMSBY

*Victoria Street, north of town centre.*
TA 271100
*Access: Can be viewed from several sides.*
This huge former steam flour mill designed by Sir W A Gelder and erected for William Marshall & Sons in 1906-7 is still one of the tallest buildings in Grimsby.   Later a grain silo for Nickersons and converted to flats in the 1990s.

### NE12 CORPORATION BRIDGE, GRIMSBY

*Across Alexandra Dock, north of town centre.*
TA 270099
*Access: Bridge crossed by public road.*
Lifting bridge erected 1869-73 and altered 1925-28 to give access over the Old Haven, now part of the Alexandra Dock, to the West Marsh area.

### NE13 NATIONAL FISHING HERITAGE CENTRE, GRIMSBY

*Next to Alexandra Dock, north of town centre.*
TA 270097
*Access: Contact 01472 323345.*
This national museum of the fishing industry includes many artefacts and interpretive settings, including a trawler at sea in the Arctic. Next to the Museum are the "Ross Tiger", one of the last trawlers out of Grimsby, and the Paddle Steamer "Lincoln Castle" built in 1940 to ferry cars and passengers between Barton-on-Humber and Hull until the Humber Bridge was opened in 1981.

### NE14 TRAMWAY DEPOT, GRIMSBY

*Victoria Street.*
TA 271097
*Access: View from public road.*
After taking over the trams in the borough, Grimsby Corporation acquired an ex-Admiralty seaplane hangar in 1926 and re-erected it as their depot.   It is now a bus garage.

NE12 : Corporation Bridge, Grimsby – KR

## NE15 YARBOROUGH HOTEL, GRIMSBY

*Next to railway station in town centre.*
TA 267092
*Access: Still a public hotel.*
Built 1851 next to the MSLR's Grimsby Town Station and still in use as a pub. Named after the Earl of Yarborough who was Chairman of the MSLR and the main landowner in this part of Lincolnshire.

## NE16 CLEETHORPES PIER

*On foreshore, next to town centre.*
TA 308090
*Access: Public access.*
The pier built in 1872-75 was 1,200ft (365.8m) long but all that remains today is a stump of 335ft (102.1m) leading to the new pavilion built in 1905 to replace one destroyed by fire. The pier was breached in 1941 as an anti-invasion precaution and most was subsequently demolished.

## NE17 AIR RAID SHELTER, CLEETHORPES

*Yarra Road; in 10 Foot at rear of houses on north side of road.*
TA 312083
*Access: No public access.*
Built by a local resident following a Zeppelin raid on 31st March 1916. Believed to be the first civilian air raid shelter ever built and now used as a private garage.

## NE18 WALTHAM WINDMILL

*At southern end of village.*
TA 259033
*Open during the summer on Sats, Suns and Bank Holidays; parties by arrangement. For further information ring 01472 822425.*
*www.walthamwindmill.co.uk*
Six-sail brick tower mill built 1879/80 by John Saunderson of Louth. 85ft high, six storeys. Restored by the former Cleethorpes District Council with the help of a local society. The only other six-sail mill is Sibsey Trader Mill (EL71).

*far left:* NE17: Air Raid Shelter, Cleethorpes – SES
*left:* NE18: Waltham Windmill – KR

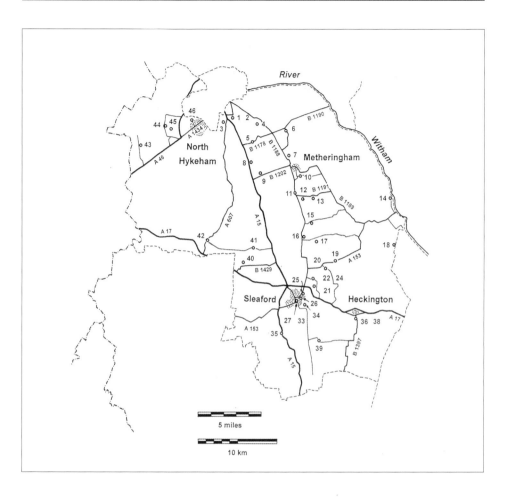

This district is south of Lincoln, on the western side of the county, and includes the small town of Sleaford as well as the southern suburbs of Lincoln and numerous rural villages. It includes the most monumental industrial remains in the county, the massive eight blocks of the Bass Maltings next to the railway line at Sleaford and the "Gothic" office block of Sleaford gas works of 1839. Close by is the preserved Heckington windmill, the only one left in the country with eight-sails. Along the eastern edge of the district is the wide flat valley of the R Witham and to the west is the narrower valley of the Upper Witham, but most of the district is on the bare uplands of the Lincoln Heath. Most villages are on or below the spring-line and the widely scattered farms on the upland still have several surviving windpumps. Before enclosure the area was so desolate that Dunston Pillar, of which the lower part still survives, was built as Britain's only land lighthouse to guide travellers across the Heath.

NK3: Service Reservoir, Bracebridge Heath – SES

NK2: Water Tower, St John's Hospital, Bracebridge Heath – SES

## NK1 ST JOHN'S HOSPITAL, BRACEBRIDGE HEATH

*On southern edge of Lincoln.*
SK 983677
*Access: Adjacent to Sleaford Road.*
Built as the County Pauper Lunatic Asylum and completed in 1852. Extensions and alterations were made through to 1939. Mostly of three-storeys the Palladian style is punctuated by Italianate towers. Now being converted mainly for residential and associated uses with new houses within its former grounds.

## NK2 ST JOHN'S HOSPITAL WATER TOWER, BRACEBRIDGE HEATH

*On southern edge of Lincoln.*
SK 983677
*Access: Visible from adjacent roads.*
A very graceful and slender use of reinforced concrete, very much the vogue in 1924-25 when this was built. The 38m (125ft) high tower was built to provide water for the former County Lunatic Asylum in the former grounds of which it stands.

**46**

## NK3 SERVICE RESERVOIR, BRACEBRIDGE HEATH

*Adjacent to A607 in this village.*
SK 977673
*Access: Can be seen from public road.*
Stone building housing a break pressure tank, designed in a Scottish Baronial style by Neil McKecknie Barron, this and its service reservoir, were built in 1908-11 by the Lincoln Corporation as part of the provision of a clean water supply to the city.

## NK4 WATER WHEEL, BRANSTON

*Alongside public footpath beyond Waterwheel Lane, west of the village centre.*
TF 018668
*Access: Public footpath passes the site.*
Cast iron waterwheel built 1879 by Charles Hett of Brigg for pumping water. Part of a private water supply system, of which much remains.

## NK5 SIGNPOST, BRANSTON

*½ mile east of Waddington airfield, on B1178 to Branston.*
TF 011647
*Access: At junction of public roads.*
Very fine 1930s cast iron finger post, fully restored using modern "fingers" in traditional style.

## NK6 POTTERHANWORTH WATER TOWER

*Alongside the road at the south end of the village.*
TF 055662
*Access: Can be seen from public road.*
Built in 1903 the brick tower incorporated rooms for the Parish Council and the Village Institute. It was converted to a house in 1995/6 including the conversion of the tank to a room.

## NK7 NOCTON MILL
*East of the B1198 between Nocton and Dunston.*
TF 058631
*Access: Can be seen from the public road.*
A five-storey mass concrete mill of 1926. It was built by Dennis' to serve the needs of their 7000 acre Nocton Estate. The estate was bought by Smiths in 1938 to produce potatoes for its new crisp factory in Lincoln. The Estate was distinctive because of the narrow gauge railway which operated from 1920 to 1969. It was several miles in extent but very few traces survive today.

## NK8 DUNSTON PILLAR
*Alongside the A15 west of Harmston village.*
TF 008619
*Access: A public footpath passes the site.*
This is the lower part of a land lighthouse built in 1751 by Sir Francis Dashwood of nearby Nocton Hall to guide travellers across the desolate expanse of the unenclosed Lincoln Heath. It was 92ft (28m) tall with a lantern on the top. After enclosure of the Heath and turnpiking of the road it was redundant and the lantern was replaced in 1810 by a coade stone statue of King George III. The statue and the top of the pillar were removed in 1940 as a possible hazard to aircraft. Part of the statue was re-erected

*above left:* NK5: Signpost, Branston – SES
*above:* NK6: Potterhanworth Water Tower – SES
*below:* NK7: Nocton Mill – SES

NK8: Dunston Pillar – SES

NK14: Timberland Pumping Station – PS

in Lincoln Castle grounds in 1974. A representation of the Pillar at its full height is shown on the tombstone of one of the masons who was killed in a fall from it at the time of its construction. The stone is on the south side of the south wall of Harmston Church.

## NK9 FORMER FLAX FACTORY, METHERINGHAM

*Alongside road from the A15 to Metheringham.*
TF 023606
*Access: No public access.*
Built during WWII to produce linen. Living quarters provided in typical WWII single-storey accommodation, now demolished. Now disused.

## NK10 ROAD BRIDGE, BLANKNEY

*Under the road from the village to Martin.*
TF 074606
*Access: Bridge carries public road; private road passing beneath.*
A private road from Blankney Hall to Metheringham railway station (opened 1882) passes under the public road here. The road was built to give privacy to the Prince of Wales and other guests of Henry Chaplin at the Hall.

## NK11 THE FIRS FARM BUILDINGS, SCOPWICK

*Alongside main road (B1188) ¼ mile N of village centre.*
TF 066584
*Access: Can be viewed from public road.*
A model or planned farmstead built for the Chaplin Estate in the early 1870s, replacing a smaller and inadequate set of buildings in the village centre.

## NK12 SCOPWICK WATERMILL (ATKIN'S)

*South of the road from Scopwick to Kirkby Green.*
TF 077579
*Access: No public access.*
Very little is known about this mill. However, with the two mills at Kirkby Green (see NK13) there is a very unusual concentration of surviving mill buildings on this short stretch of Scopwick Beck. The reason for this is that the limestone Lincolnshire Heath has no surface water but Scopwick lies on the spring line at a point where the water flow was particularly strong.

## NK13 WATERMILLS, KIRKBY GREEN

*Manor Mill, west of the ford on road to Rowston; Young's Mill, south of road half way between Kirkby Green and level crossing.*
TF 084577 and TF 088580
*Access: No public access; can be seen from the road.*
There are surviving buildings of two watermills here, both flour mills. **Young's Mill** (TF 088580) worked until the 1930s and **Manor Mill** (TF 084577) until 1935. See also NK12 Scopwick Mill.

## NK14 TIMBERLAND PUMPING STATION

*W bank of Witham, 1 mile north of Tattershall Bridge.*
TF 189583
*Access: View from road.*
Built 1839 with a beam engine driving a scoop wheel. In 1881 the beam engine was replaced by a more powerful Tuxford high pressure en-

gine which in turn was replaced by a Ruston diesel in 1938 after the chimney had been struck by lightning. It drove a Gwynnes pump which had been installed in 1924.

## NK15 DIGBY RAILWAY STATION
*South of Station Road, Digby.*
TF 088550
*Access: No public access.*
The GN&GEJR, for its line opened in 1882 between Spalding and Lincoln, had a very distinctive style of architecture for its stations. The line remains open but all of its original stations were closed and most buildings demolished. Digby survives, with its typical single-storey range of two end pavilions linked with a range fronted by a platform awning.

## NK16 DORRINGTON WATER TOWER
*Beside B1188 north of village*
TF 076532
*Access: Can be seen from nearby public road.*
An early (1910) rural water tower, small and disused but still in good condition. Sleaford Rural District Council was well in advance of its time for the provision of village water supplies.

## NK17 NORTH INGS FARM RAILWAY, DORRINGTON
*South of the minor road, about ½ a mile east of the village.*
TF 098528
*Access: Open to visitors on 1st Sunday of month, April to October. 01529 414294 for details.*
This narrow-gauge railway was laid as a farm railway in 1972 and opened as a museum in 1990. It operates both steam and diesel locomotives by manufacturers such as Ruston and Hornsby, Listers and Motor Rail from former light railways in Lincolnshire and elsewhere.

## NK18 BOTTOM LOCK, NORTH KYME
*1½ miles along towpath from Chapel Hill.*
TF 196523
*Access: by public towpath on south bank of Kyme Eau.*
The Sleaford Navigation was opened in 1794 and closed in 1881 but it is still in water. Bottom Lock, which is 2 miles above the junction with the R Witham, was restored in the 1980s and re-opened the lower two thirds of the canal to river craft once again.

## NK19 VILLAGE SMITHY, ANWICK
*In centre of village, south side of A153.*
TF 116505
*Access: View from main road.*
Two slate-roofed conical pavilions are joined with a rectangular link. One end houses the Smithy, the other living accommodation. The former Shoeing Shed and living quarters are within the link. Dating from around 1800 with later alterations, the building re-opened in 2003 and now produces decorative ironwork which can be seen in the on-site gallery.

## NK20 CANAL BRIDGE AND LOCK, HAVERHOLME, EWERBY
*3 miles north-east of Sleaford, on road from A163 to Ewerby.*
TF 105497
*Access: Bridge crossed by public road, lock to the west reached by towpath. Car park on south side of bridge.*
A fine stone bridge of 1893 to carry a minor road over the Slea Navigation, probably of this quality as it was close to the now demolished mansion of the Earl of Winchilsea. The lock was converted into a boathouse but its corrugated iron roof has now gone. Alongside it is a pumphouse, the now empty chamber having above it the remains of the pump, the latter manufactured by Hett of Brigg.

NK16: Dorrington Water Tower – KR

NK19: Village Smithy, Anwick – SES

**49**

## NK22 HOLDINGHAM LOCK

*On footpath between Sleaford and Haverholme.*
TF 088479
*Access: From footpath alongside navigation.*
On the New River Slea or Mill Stream which was made navigable in 1794. The chamber has brick walls with iron reinforcing bands and stone cappings. The restoration of the Navigation has not yet reached this point.

## NK23 CANAL TOLL BOOTH, HOLDINGHAM

*On footpath between Sleaford and Holdingham.*
TF 089480
*Access: Visible from footpath alongside navigation.*
Curiously sited, only 2 miles from the head of the navigation in Sleaford, this small, eight sided building could only have been a booth for collecting tolls from users of the canal.

## NK24 HOLDINGHAM WATERMILL

*Beside navigation, opposite public footpath between Sleaford and Holdingham.*
TF 089479
*Access: Visible from footpath alongside navigation.*
This corn mill was built early in C19 by Samuel Cropper and ceased working before the last miller sold it in 1962. Its wooden undershot wheel with an iron axle still remains under a pantile roof at the side of the building, and there is said to be much machinery and equipment still inside.

## NK25 SLEAFORD GAS WORKS

*Eastgate, about ½ a mile east of town centre.*
TF 076464
*Access: No public access but can be seen alongside the road.*
The offices of 1839 still survive with a Victorian Gothic façade to the road. Now converted to house modern offices.

## NK26 COGGLESFORD WATERMILL AND LOCK, SLEAFORD

*East Road, about 200 yards east of District Council Offices.*
TF 074461
*Access: Cogglesford Mill, admission free.*
*Open afternoons daily Easter Monday to end of September, and at weekends rest of year. For details ring 01529 414294. www.tic.oden.co.uk*
The top lock of the Navigation still survives with the gates having been replaced by a sluice. Alongside is the Mill, probably built in 1771 with

## NK21 EVEDON WATER TOWER

*Alongside the road at the west end of the village.*
TF 094476
*Access: No public access to the interior.*
Built in 1915 for the Sleaford RDC this tower became redundant in the 1960s. In 1989 it was extended and converted to a private house, losing its tank in the process.

NK22, 23, 24: Lock, Toll-Booth and Watermill, Holdingham – NRW

*above:* NK26: Cogglesford Watermill – SES
*below:* NK27: Navigation Weighing Office, Sleaford: SES

a top floor added in the 1830s, and restored in the early 1990s. It has a breast shot wheel and is open to the public.

### NK27 NAVIGATION WHARF AND WEIGHING OFFICE, SLEAFORD
*Carre Street.*
TF 069457
*Access: Public access to the Yard and The Hub.*
This was the terminus of the navigation opened in 1794 and closed in 1881. The yard includes the former stone built weighing office of 1838/9 which carries the coat of arms of the Navigation on its front elevation. An early warehouse of 1794 has been converted to offices and a later seed warehouse dating from the 1930s has been incorporated into a Craft Centre known as The Hub, opened in 2003.

### NK28 NAVIGATION CUT, SLEAFORD
*Carre Street.*
TF 070457
*Can be seen from public road and footpath.*
A loop was cut on the south bank to enable vessels to turn, in lieu of a basin. This created an island on which several industrial buildings were erected. Part of this cut has been filled in but some of it can still be seen.

*Left:* NK29: Money's Mill, Sleaford – SES
*above:* NK31: Picturedrome, Sleaford – NRW

## NK29 MONEY'S MILL, SLEAFORD
*Money's Yard, off Southgate.*
TF 068457
*Access: Mill stands within a public car park; no public access to interior.*
This brick tower windmill was built c1794 at the head of the Slea Navigation in place of an earlier post mill in the same position. It originally had three sets of stones. It was raised to 70ft (21.3m) in 1810, eight-storeys high, and had four-sails and worked until 1912. It now lacks sails and machinery but is structurally intact. It was saved from demolition in the 1980s by Sleaford and District Civic Trust and for a time was the town's Tourist Information Centre but in early 2004 was awaiting a change of use.

## NK30 ELECTRICITY WORKS, SLEAFORD
*Electric Station Road.*
TF 063457
*Can be seen from public road.*
This was built in 1901, quite early for a town the size of Sleaford. The buildings are now used as a sub-station.

## NK31 PICTUREDROME, SLEAFORD
*Southgate.*
TF 069455
*Can be seen from public road.*
The Picturedrome of 1920 continued to show films until 2002 and was the oldest cinema in the county still showing films. It has been converted to a club.

## NK32 SLEAFORD RAILWAY STATION
*Station Road.*
TF 068454
*Access: Public access to platforms, waiting rooms and footbridge.*
This is still a country junction station today. The original stone building of 1857 is sandwiched between red brick extensions of 1882, when its importance was increased with the opening of the GN&GEJR. At either end of the station limits traditional GNR signal boxes still control the trains and access to the remaining sidings. Goods Shed demolished 2004.

## NK33 SEED WAREHOUSES, SLEAFORD

*Station Road, next to Railway Station.*
TF 068455
*Access: No public access to the interior.*

Charles Sharpe & Co exported seeds from Sleaford worldwide and had several warehouses in the town. Since the firm closed c1990 two C19 warehouses have been converted, one for commercial use the other to flats.

## NK34 BASS MALTINGS, SLEAFORD

*East of Sleaford railway station, behind the Carre Arms Hotel.*
TF 074452
*Can be seen from public road.*

One of the major industrial monuments in Lincolnshire. It consists of eight maltings with a central block of engine house and workshops with a row of staff cottages on the access road. They were built 1899-1905 for Bass, Ratcliff and Gretton of Burton on Trent to the design of HA Couchman. It is the largest complex of its kind outside Burton with a total frontage of almost 1000 ft (305m). It closed in 1960 and the two Robey engines were removed to museums. When built, the maltings were highly automated and very advanced with bridges, elevators and conveyor belts to connect all parts of the complex. Three blocks were badly damaged by fire in 1976 but their walls still stand to full height. Only a small part is in industrial use today but in 2003 North Kesteven District Council commissioned a study on the future of the buildings.

## NK35 TURNPIKE MILE POSTS, SLEAFORD

*Alongside A15 Sleaford to Peterborough road.*
TF 049419 and elsewhere
*Access: can be seen from road.*

Several mileposts remain on the A15 from Sleaford to Peterborough which was turnpiked in 1756 as part of a long route from Norman Cross (on the Great North Road) to Lincoln.

## NK36 HECKINGTON WINDMILL

*Adjacent to the Railway Station.*
TF 144435
*Open daily 12 to 5 mid-July to mid-September, Sundays 2 to 5 for rest of year, and other days in spring and autumn. For info and Group Bookings ring 01529 461919.*

The only remaining eight-sailed tower mill in England retains its sails and most of its internal equipment. There were few mills with so much power and it had five pairs of stones although only three pairs were worked at any one

NK34: Bass Maltings, Sleaford – CJL

time. The tower was built in 1830 and the cap and sails were brought from Boston in 1892 after fire destroyed the original woodwork. It is owned by Lincolnshire County Council and underwent a major refit in 2003/04.

## NK37 HECKINGTON RAILWAY STATION
*Station Road.*
TF 146435
*Access: Public Access to platforms.*
*Booking Office and Waiting Room now a museum –*
*Open Saturdays, Sundays and Bank Holidays 12 – 5.*
Opened in 1859 the station is still open. The Goods Shed and Station House are in commercial use. The Booking Office and Waiting Room are a museum with exhibits relating to the history of the station and the GNR and LNER. The signal box, built c1880, still operates semaphore signals and the level crossing retains traditional gates (see front cover).

## NK38 PEA ROOM, HECKINGTON
*Adjacent to the Railway Station.*
TF 146437
*Access: No public access to the interior.*
This red brick warehouse of 1890 was built for the sorting and packing of peas.

## NK39 PACKHORSE BRIDGE, SCREDINGTON
*Northbeck, Scredington.*
TF 097409
*Access: Alongside public road.*
A two-arched medieval packhorse bridge of c1250, now carrying a footpath over the village stream.

## NK40 COLLEGE HALL AND GUARDHOUSE, CRANWELL
*5 miles north-west of Sleaford, 2 miles west of Cranwell village.*
TF 000499
*Access: Can be viewed from public road.*
The Royal Naval Air Service opened an airfield at Cranwell in 1916 and the Royal Air Force College was built here 1929-33 in a neo-Georgian style by J.G.West. The high dome is visible for a long distance around, as well as its flashing beacon which can be seen from the coast 30 miles away. A railway branch line from Sleaford opened in 1917 and closed to passengers in 1927 and goods in 1956. The former railway station is now the Guardhouse south of the road.

NK38: Pea Room, Heckington – SES

## NK41 GIN HOUSE, BRAUNCEWELL
*5 miles north of Sleaford, on minor road west of the A15.*
TF 013519
*Access: Alongside south side of road through village. Interpretation Board on site.*
A rare survival in this part of the country. The gin house for a bone mill is largely complete. It was of the overhead type where the horse was tethered to a beam over the top. Built c1800 it is polygonal in shape and was originally open-sided with a thatched roof.

## NK42 LEADENHAM RAILWAY STATION
*Alongside the A607 at the north end of the village.*
SK 958529
*Access: No public access, can be seen from the road.*
This GNR branch line opened in 1867. As this station straddled the parish boundary the station house and road bridge in Leadenham were, at the insistence of the landowners, built of Ancaster stone but the goods shed and bridge to the north are of red brick as they are in Welbourn parish. The line closed in 1965 and the station is now a private house while the goods shed is in industrial use. The gateway to the industrial premises is a re-sited original GNR gate and piers.

## NK43 SWINDERBY RAILWAY STATION
*1 mile north of Swinderby village.*
SK 868643
*Access: Station still open for passengers.*
Built in 1846 by the MR this was on the first line of railway built in Lincolnshire and retains many of its original buildings. It also has the last surviving MR Signal Box in situ in the County.

NK39: Packhorse Bridge, Scredington – SES

## NK44 RAILWAY STATION, THORPE ON THE HILL

*On the road to Whisby, north of the village.*
SK 902665
*Access: Can be seen from the road, no public access.*
1846 MR station building of *cottage ornee* design. It has a curved elevation to the track and a steep, overhanging roof. The station is closed but the line remains open.

## NK45 NORTH HYKEHAM AND WHISBY – SAND AND GRAVEL

*Whisby Road, signposted to the west of the A46 Lincoln Bypass.*
TF 911662 (entrance)
*Access: A nature reserve with public access.*
Very extensive area of pits, several now used for recreation and nature conservation. Some still in use.

## NK46 ENGINEERING WORKS, NORTH HYKEHAM

*Next to Hykeham Railway Station.*
SK 936674
*Access: Can be seen from road.*
Harrison's Malleable Iron Works moved here from a site in Lincoln in late C19, and the premises have since changed hands several times.

NK41: Horse Gin, Brauncewell – SES

**55**

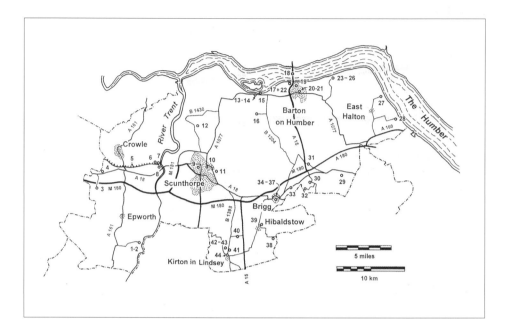

This district extends across the northern edge of the historic county from the Isle of Axholme in the west along the south bank of the Humber to the edge of Immingham Dock and the North Sea. It includes the northern end of two stretches of Lincolnshire's uplands, the Wolds in the east and the Lincoln Edge in the west, and is dominated by the iron and steel town of Scunthorpe. Although created since the 1860s, there are few remains of Scunthorpe's 19th century ironworks which were replaced by new plant during the 20th century, but in the town itself there are still some early streets of housing. The district also has the small towns of Brigg and Barton on Humber, the former railway settlements of New Holland and Barnetby, and several rural villages including some on the banks of the Humber and the Trent that used to depend on water transport. Parts of the district in the Isle and the Ancholme valley are low-lying land reclaimed by land drainage. The south bank of the Humber is lined with the remains of former brick and tile-works which used water transport to serve distant markets. Distinctive industrial monuments in the district are the postmill at Wrawby and Sir John Rennie's suspension bridge over the Ancholme at Horkstow as well as the Humber Bridge. In the east of the district is the navigable R Ancholme and through the Isle runs the eastern end of the Stainforth and Keadby Canal.

### NL1 PUMPING STATION, OWSTON FERRY

*3 miles S-E of Epworth.*
SK 813995
*Access: Visible from adjacent main road, and
occasionally open to the public.*
This was built in 1910 to pump water from 5,000
acres in the southern part of the Isle of Axholme
into the Trent.   The station contains one of its
original Marshall class 'L' double expansion reciprocating steam engines (not used since
1963), a Ruston & Hornsby class 8HRC diesel
engine installed in 1952 and a later Lister
Blackstone engine.

### NL2 WAREHOUSES, OWSTON FERRY

*3 miles S-E of Epworth.*
SK 813999
*Access: Visible from road on river bank.*
Most villages on the banks of the Trent had
warehouses for goods carried on the river.  This
example has a 1900s house built onto the river
end, implying a change of use at that time.

### NL3 TROLLEYBUS MUSEUM, SANDTOFT, BELTON

*3 miles W of Belton.*
SE 751082
*Access: Annual programme of open days, tel: 01724
711391.*
Home of the largest collection of trolley buses
in the UK.

### NL4 DIRTNESS PUMPING STATION, CROWLE

*3 miles S-W of Crowle.*
SE 749098
*Access: View from minor road on south side of drain to
south of A18.*
A beam engine house built in 1867 in poly-
chrome brick housing two 50hp Watt engines
driving a 10.1m (33ft) dia scoop wheel which
was capable of lifting 1200 tonnes of water per
hour.  Still in use to house electric pumps.

*left:* NL2: Warehouse, Owston Ferry – CJL
*above:* NL4: Dirtness Pumping Station – CJL

NL8: Keadby Bridge – KH

## NL5 STAINFORTH AND KEADBY CANAL, CROWLE

*Mile S of village.*
SE 784110
*Access: Can be seen from public road.*

The Stainforth and Keadby Canal was authorised in 1793 and opened in 1802 to bypass the lower reaches of the R Dun navigation in Yorkshire. It was built to take 200 ton coastal vessels as far inland as Thorne in Yorkshire. There is a wharf at Crowle where the main road through the Isle of Axholme crosses the canal. The SYR purchased the canal and opened a branch to Keadby along the north bank in 1859. Half a mile east is an embankment which used a large swing bridge to carry the Axholme Joint Railway (opened 1905) over the canal and the 1859 railway.

## NL6 CANAL DRAWBRIDGE, KEADBY

*3½ miles E of Crowle.*
SE 826114
*Access: Public access to nearby road bridge over canal.*

A very unusual horizontal steel drawbridge taking the Doncaster-Scunthorpe railway across the Stainforth and Keadby Canal, built 1925/26 by Sir Wm. Arrol & Co., Glasgow. The moveable steel deck, which crosses the canal at an oblique angle, is hauled clear of the canal into a recess in the south bank by steel cables and electric motors.

## NL7 TIDAL LOCK AND RAILWAY STATION, KEADBY

*4 miles E of Crowle.*
SE 835114
*Access: Public access from adjacent main road.*

The tidal lock at Keadby gave access to the Stainforth and Keadby Canal from the R Trent. The SYR opened a branch to Keadby along

the north bank of the canal in 1859. Its original terminus next to the lock became a siding when the line was extended to Scunthorpe via Keadby Bridge five years later.

## NL8 KEADBY BRIDGE

*Over R Trent, 3 miles W of Scunthorpe.*
SE 841106
*Access: Public access across bridge and along E bank of river.*

The Scherzer rolling lift bridge was built by GCR in 1912-16 to take road and rail traffic across the Trent. When built it was the largest of its kind in Europe. Designed by James Ball, contractor Sir Wm. Arrol & Co. This bridge was electrically powered from the start; the powerhouse still survives under the bridge abutment. It replaced a swing bridge built 1861 by SYR to gain access for trains to the newly-discovered ironstone at Scunthorpe. The lifting span was fastened down c1960 and it has not been lifted since.

## NL9 SCUNTHORPE MUSEUM AND ART GALLERY

*Oswald Road, central Scunthorpe.*
SE 891109
*Access: Tue. to Sat. 10am-4pm; closed Mondays.*
*01724 843533.*

This museum includes material about local industries.

## NL10 INDUSTRIAL HOUSING, SCUNTHORPE

*South of railway, ½ mile east of railway station, off Rowland Road.*
SE 900108
*Access: Can be viewed from street.*

The few streets of New Frodingham laid out by landowner Rowland Winn in 1865-70 were intended to be the centre of the new community on the ironstone field, but instead people chose Scunthorpe half a mile away. The houses were of good quality, and the streets are wider than usual.

## NL11 CORUS STEEL WORKS, SCUNTHORPE

*East side of town; Brigg Road, Frodingham.*
SE 915033
*Access: Can be viewed from public roads.*

The modern steel works was built in 1970-73 to re-develop the Appleby-Frodingham and Redbourne works. The Bloom and Billet Mill must be the longest industrial building in the county at around 1.3km (1,420yds).

## NL12 NORMANBY PARK, SCUNTHORPE

*3 miles N of Scunthorpe.*
SE 886167
*Access: A public park, open daily.*
The former home of the Sheffield family is now a country park and museum operated by North Lincolnshire Council. It includes a farming museum, with material on local industries.

## NL13 CEMENT FACTORY, SOUTH FERRIBY

*3½ miles W of Barton on Humber.*
SE 973209
*Access: Can be seen from road.*
Large early C20 factory served by overhead conveyor belt from chalk quarry to the east.

## NL14 SLUICE AND TIDAL LOCK, SOUTH FERRIBY

*3½ miles W of Barton on Humber.*
SE 975210
*Can be accessed from public road.*
This tidal outfall sluice was built in 1842-44 by Sir John Rennie on the site of earlier sluices of 1640 and c1769 to separate the Ancholme Navigation from the tidal Humber. It incorporates a lock which was crossed by a road on a swing bridge; the bridge was renewed in 1982. The original upstream timber pointing doors have been replaced (mid C20) with steel vertical lifting gates. A small building nearby was formerly the offices of the Ancholme Commissioners.

## NL15 HUMBER SLOOP, 'AMY HOWSON', AT SOUTH FERRIBY

*Often moored on Ancholme, close to South Ferriby Sluice.*
SE 975208
*Access: Can be seen from public road at Ferriby Sluice.*
The Humber Keel and Sloop Preservation Society has restored two of the traditional sailing craft of the Humber and its adjacent waterways, and the sloop 'Amy Howson' is rigged fore and aft. During the winter she is often moored at Clapson's Marina near Ferriby Sluice. She is a steel hulled vessel built at Beverley in 1914, and after 1924 she was mainly engaged in carrying oil seed from Hull to the Yarborough Mills (now demolished) at Brigg. Her sister vessel the square-rigged keel 'Comrade' is based at Hull in Yorkshire but is occasionally seen on the south bank of the Humber.

## NL16 HORKSTOW BRIDGE

*At end of minor road from B1204 N of Horkstow.*
SE 973190
*Access: by public road.*
This little known gem of civil engineering was designed by Sir John Rennie and built in 1834 at the end of a cul-de-sac to give access to fields on the other side of the R Ancholme. The original masonry and ironwork remain, making it one of the oldest suspension bridges in Britain, and it still has a simple plank deck over the span of 130ft 6in (39.8m) (see back cover). **59**

NL17: William Blythe's Tile Works, Barton on Humber – KH

NL18: Humber Bridge – KH

NL20: Ropewalk, Barton on Humber – KR

### NL17 TILE WORKS, BARTON ON HUMBER

*On south bank of Humber, west of Humber Bridge.*
TA 022233
*Access via public footpath on foreshore west of Humber Bridge.*
Operated by Blyth's Tile Yard. The yard is fully operational producing flat and pantiles etc and includes claypit, pugmill, drying sheds and kilns, all clearly visible from the Humber Bridge. This works has the distinction of operating the last surviving brickyard railway in Britain.

### NL18 HUMBER BRIDGE

*Main road A15 crosses the bridge.*
TA 024246
*Access: Viewed from Barton on Humber, and from viewing area on north bank.*
Toll bridge designed by Freeman, Fox & Partners, built by a consortium of contractors and opened by H.M. Queen Elizabeth II on 24th June 1981 after eight years construction. It was for a period the World's longest span suspension bridge with a central span of 4,626ft (1,410m). It links Lincolnshire and Yorkshire with a single carriageway road, footway and cycle track.

### NL19 HAVEN, BARTON ON HUMBER

*Waterside Road, at northern end of town.*
TA 029230
*Access: Haven anytime, coast guard station by arrangement with North Lincolnshire Council. The remainder is private property visible from Waterside Road.*
Until the 1840s Barton was the terminus of the main ferry across the Humber to Hull, at the end of a stage coach service from London (see also NL23). Features remaining beside the Haven are the inn used by travellers and the former coastguard station and coastguard cottages (Humber Terrace). The boat yard operated until 1974 by the Clapson family is now used for the construction of steel vessels.

### NL20 ROPEWALK, BARTON ON HUMBER

*Next to Proudfoot Supermarket off Malt Kiln Lane.*
TA 029230
*Access: Tuesday – Saturday 10am to 5pm; Sundays and Bank Holidays 10am to 4pm; Phone 01652 660380.*
Along the east bank of the Haven is a very long single-storey brick building with a pantiled roof which was formerly the longest covered ropewalk in the country. Nearby a former warehouse with hipped roof and iron wall crane, all part of Hall's Barton Ropery until 1989. Part of rope walk building now houses heritage exhibition and contemporary art and craft studios and gallery.

### NL21 TOWER MILL, BARTON ON HUMBER

*Off Market Place.*
TA 032218
*Access: Now a pub restaurant.*
Seven-storey brick tower mill built c1810 with adjoining later C19 granaries converted to pub/restaurant. This former six-sailed windmill

NL21: Tower windmill, Barton on Humber – NRW

ground corn and chalk for whiting. The tower and corn grinding machinery are preserved. This mill and a derelict tower mill off Waterside Road are the sole survivors of a number of mills within the town grinding grain and chalk.

## NL22 BRICKYARDS, BARTON ON HUMBER

*Far Ings Road gives access to brick yards to the west of the Humber Bridge. Park in Humber Bridge Viewing Area car park.*
TA 041234
*Access: Can be seen from footpath along Humber bank.*
Water-filled lagoons stretch along the whole length of Barton's shoreline, indicating the position of brickyards which worked during the C19 and C20. There were large reserves of

good quality clay and this area sent great quantities of bricks by water inland to Yorkshire and round the coast to East Anglia and London. Two of the yards still produce pantiles but others are used as nature reserves or for sailing and angling.

## NL23 RAILWAY PIER, NEW HOLLAND

*At north end of village, projecting into Humber.*
TA 080246
*Access: No public access, can be seen from footpath on Humber bank E and W.*
This 1,375ft (419m) long pier was the eastern terminus of the MSLR, where passengers caught the ferry across the Humber to Hull. The original timber pier of 1848 was replaced by a steel one (encased in concrete) in 1923-28 and the upstream and downstream arms of the pierhead were replaced in 1935-39 and 1946-49 respectively. The planks supporting the slope of the upstream arm were a very early structural use of pre-cast pre-stressed concrete in the country. There were stations at each end of the pier but both closed and the ferry ended when the Humber Bridge opened on 24th June 1981. The pier and the pier-head station buildings are in use as a bulk handling facility but the old station at the landward end has been demolished.

## NL24 DOCK, NEW HOLLAND

*On foreshore, E of Pier.*
TA 082244
*Access: Can be seen from public footpath.*
A tidal dock built by MSLR in 1848 and used by BR until 1960; the basin is now badly silted.

## NL25 MANCHESTER SQUARE, NEW HOLLAND

*On E side of road, in centre of village.*
TA 083239
*A public square.*
The MSLR also had a locomotive shed, works, laundry and other premises at the terminus and

NL25: Manchester Square, New Holland – NRW

a small railway community developed, of which the main evidence is Manchester Square, built 1849, with 2-storey houses round three sides of a square. The houses were renovated in the early 1980s. North of the square is the Yarborough Arms, now the Lincoln Castle Hotel.

## NL26 BRICKYARDS, NEW HOLLAND
*On Humber bank, mainly W of Pier.*
TA 088244 westwards
*Access: Can be seen from public footpath on Humber bank.*
Water-filled lagoons stretching along the south bank of the Humber indicate the site of a significant industry producing tiles and bricks which were exported by water to Yorkshire, East Anglia and London in the late 19th century.

## NL27 BRICK KILN, EAST HALTON
*On Humber bank 2 miles N-E of East Halton.*
TA 156212
*Access: Can be seen from public road.*
One of the few remaining Scotch kilns of the brick making industry that once stretched all along the south bank of the Humber.

## NL28 LIGHTHOUSES, SOUTH KILLINGHOLME
*About 2 miles east of village, on bank of Humber.*
TA 178183
*Access: Public footpath along Humber Bank.*
A trio of lighthouses close to each other: South Low (1836) by Francis Dales, North Low (1851 - now a house) by William Foale, and High rebuilt 1876-77.

## NL29 HUMBERSIDE INTERNATIONAL AIRPORT, KIRMINGTON
*3 miles E of Barnetby le Wold.*
TA 096104
*Access: An operational airport.*
This was created on the site of RAF Kirmington in 1974 and is of local rather than regional significance.

## NL30 BARNETBY RAILWAY STATION
*Station Road.*
TA 054099
*Access: Anytime.*
Rebuilt by GCR in 1915 in Queen Anne style, to replace the original MSLR station of 1848, following quadrupling of the line between Wrawby junction and Brocklesby to cope with extra traffic from Immingham Dock. Some old stone sleeper blocks are used as platform edging.

NL29: Humberside International Airport – CJL

NL31: Granary and Cartshed, Elsham
Top Farm – JAS

## NL31 GRANARY AND CARTSHED, ELSHAM TOP FARM, ELSHAM

*North-east of junction of M180 and A15.*
TA 052118
*Access: Can be viewed from road.*
Farm buildings around a yard. Superb example of chalk construction, listed Grade II*. Built in 1840s by T G Corbett, Lord of the Manor of Elsham and restored 1990.

## NL32 RAILWAY SIGNAL BOX, WRAWBY

*Wrawby Moor, mile west of Barnetby le Wold.*
TA 045092
*Access: Can be seen from minor road and public footpath to S.*
Built in 1916 at the intersection of three busy lines of the GCR. Until 2000 when it was refurbished it was the largest manually operated signal box in the country.

## NL33 POST WINDMILL, WRAWBY

*North east of Brigg*
TA 026088
*Access: Summer open day. Phone 01652 653699.*
The last of hundreds of post mills once at work in the county. Remodelled from earlier mill on site 1832; worked by wind until 1939; restored to working order 1960s. Two storied wooden body containing millstones and four spring sails mounted on post above brick roundhouse.

## NL34 CONEY COURT, BRIGG

*Narrow lane off N side of Market Place.*
SE 000072
*Access: Public alleyway.*
Site of factory where hats and muffs were made from rabbit skins, Brigg's main industry until c1830.

## NL35 OLD RIVER ANCHOLME, BRIGG

*West of Market Place.*
SE 998072
*Access: river side walks through the centre of Brigg, and Cadney Road.*
After the straightening and improvement of the Ancholme by Sir John Rennie was completed in 1828, a loop of the old river was enlarged and deepened in 1830/31 for craft to reach the town centre, but most of the industrial buildings which used to line its banks have been demolished.

**63**

NL33: Post Windmill, Wrawby – KR

## NL36 COUNTY BRIDGE, BRIGG

*Between Market Place and Bridge Street.*
SE 998072
*Access: anytime.*
Road bridge with 40ft (12.2m) span over old R Ancholme designed by J S Padley, County Surveyor, and built by George Willoughby of York, contractor, in 1828. The parapets were replaced by modern railings in the 1960s.

## NL37 YARBOROUGH BRIDGE, BRIGG

*Bridge Street/Scawby Road.*
SE 993069
*Access: from car park at Leisure Centre.*
Built 1827 across New River Ancholme with 60ft (18.3m) span. Designed by Sir John Rennie. Widened sympathetically by reconstructing southern façade further south.   North of the bridge on the west bank stood the large Yarborough Oil and Cake Mill demolished in the 1990s.

## NL38 ANCHOLME BRIDGE, HIBALDSTOW

*2 miles east of Hibaldstow.*
TA 004015
*Access: public road from west.*
Road bridge of 1889 over the new R Ancholme to the east of Hibaldstow.   Designed by Alfred Atkinson; iron work by Porter & Co. of Lincoln.

## NL39 HIBALDSTOW WIND AND WATERMILL

*On N-E edge of village.*
SE 982027
*Access: View from road; this is a private house.*
This rare combined mill still contains some of its equipment although it has lost the cap, sails and waterwheel.   The tower emerges above the first floor of which there are 8 radial vaulted rooms, some of which were lived in at one time.

**64**

*above left:* NL37: Yarborough Bridge, Brigg – NRW
*above:* NL39: Wind and Watermill, Hibaldstow: NRW

## NL40 SIGNAL BOX AND LIME KILN, HIBALDSTOW

*Gainsthorpe Road near Kirton Lindsey.*
SE 948013
*Access: View from road.*
Last surviving GCR high level signal box controlling sidings to large former stone quarries and lime works. Nearby are impressive remains of Victorian Lime Kiln, constructed of limestone and brick, adjacent to railway line.

## NL41 MOUNT PLEASANT MILL, KIRTON IN LINDSEY

*North Cliff Road, Kirton Lindsey.*
SK 939994
*Open daily except Mondays 10am to 5pm.   Phone 01652 640177.*
Four-storey tower mill in full working order producing organically grown flours and open to public with adjoining tea room and shop. Built 1875 to replace earlier post mill and worked commercially until 1973, latterly using Crossley oil engine. Mill restored to wind power 1991 and retains all its machinery below the curb. Iron work by Marshalls of Gainsborough. Two pairs of stones wind-powered, one pair on ground floor hurst frame.

## NL42 RAILWAY TUNNEL, KIRTON IN LINDSEY

*To the east of Kirton in Lindsey station.*
SK 937001
*Access: visible from Kirton in Lindsey Station.*
The turreted southern portal of one of the few railway tunnels in Lincolnshire, on the MSLR main line to Grimsby opened in 1849. It is 1,333yds (1,219m) long, and was the first in Lincolnshire. The engineer was John Fowler.

## NL43 GREAT CENTRAL STATION, KIRTON IN LINDSEY

*North of the town.*
SK 934996
*Access: View from Station Yard and the platform.*
Station building now a private house but platform to single track railway line still in use. An MSLR rural station built 1849, architects Weightman and Hadfield. Nearby former goods warehouse, and coal drops.

## NL44 MALTINGS, KIRTON IN LINDSEY

*Station Road, north of village.*
SK 934996
*Access: View from public road.*
Malting range complete but in 2003 disused and for sale. Built to be serviced by nearby MSLR line.

*above left:* NL41: Mount Pleasant Windmill, Kirton in Lindsey – KR
*left:* NL42: Railway Tunnel, Kirton in Lindsey – KR
*far above:* NL43: Railway Station, Kirton in Lindsey – JAS
*above:* NL44: Maltings, Kirton in Lindsey – KR

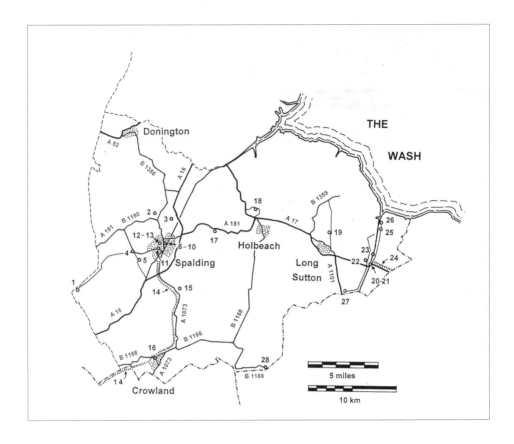

This district of wide open spaces in the south-east corner of Lincolnshire is at the heart of the fens, with Cambridgeshire to the south and Norfolk to the east. It includes the town and former port of Spalding, the village of Sutton Bridge with many interesting industrial remains, and the small towns of Holbeach and Long Sutton as well as several small villages. Most of the district has been reclaimed from the sea to the north and the fens to the south, and it is crossed by impressive man made drainage systems and long straight roads to serve some of the richest agricultural land in Britain. There used to be six railways radiating out of Spalding making it a significant local junction, but now only two remain, to Sleaford and Peterborough respectively. There were a number of turnpike roads in the district, and there are still plenty of well-maintained milestones on all six former turnpike roads out of Spalding, and cast iron finger posts in the area. The area also includes the unusual Sneath's windmill at Lutton Gowts and the towering Moulton windmill, now being restored, as well as a range of interesting bridges.

SH2: Flax Mill, Pinchbeck – CJL

## SH1 SIR GILBERT HEATHCOTE'S TUNNEL, DEEPING FEN/BOURNE FEN

*Tongue End, 3 miles E of Bourne.*
TF 148181
*Access: Public footpath along south bank of river.*

C18 drainage tunnel under the R Glen near Tongue End.

## SH2 FLAX MILL, PINCHBECK

*At north end of village.*
TF 242266
*Access: View from public road.*

Large building and associated outbuildings comprising former flax mill. Much modernised and in use for mixed industrial applications. The end of the main building is marked 1851.

## SH3 BEAM ENGINE, PINCHBECK MARSH PUMPING STATION

*Mile N of Spalding.*
TF 262262
*Access: Open daily during the summer months.*

Built 1833 and ceased operating 1952, this was the last steam driven scoop wheel drainage engine to work in the fens. The Welland and Deepings Internal Drainage Board then diverted the drain to the new engine house along-side so that the old one could be preserved. The engine by the Butterley Company is a single-cylinder rotative A-frame beam engine of 20nhp and is the oldest such engine in situ. It drove the 22ft (6.7m) dia. scoop wheel to drain about 4,000 acres.

## SH4 PODE HOLE PUMPING STATION, PINCHBECK

*2 miles west of Spalding.*
TF 213220
*Access: Visible from adjacent main road.*

At one time this was the largest steam installation in the fens, but the engines installed in 1825 ceased in 1925 and were scrapped in 1952. The building remains and the Drainage Board have a small drainage museum. Modern electric and diesel engined pumping stations are still operational at the same location. The original byelaws are still displayed on a massive wooden notice board on the wall of the old pumphouse.

## SH5 HORSESHOE BRIDGE, SPALDING COMMON

*2 miles W of Spalding.*
TF 219211
*Access: Public road across bridge.*

Very early reinforced concrete road bridge of 1910/12, 45ft (13.7m) span, with archaic parapet-beam design. Designed by L G Mouchel and Partners for the Deeping Fen Trustees, using the Hennebique System of Ferro-Concrete construction. A steel deck has recently been added to reduce the loading on the original concrete structure.

## SH6 WAREHOUSES, SPALDING

*On both banks of Welland in town centre.*
TF 251228
*Access: Can be seen from public roads and paths.*

Sea-going boats sailed up to the town until

*below:* SH4: Pode Hole Pumping Station, Pinchbeck – CJL
*right:* SH5: Horseshoe Bridge, Spalding Common – CJL

SH6: Warehouse, Double Street, Spalding – CJL

SH9: Blacksmith's Shop, Spalding – CJL

c1914 and there are still remains of some warehouses on each bank of the R Welland, including an old one in Double Street.

### SH7 ALBION MILL, SPALDING
*W bank of river, N of town centre.*
*TF 252232*
*Can be seen from public road*
Four-storey C19 steam flour mill later converted to head office of Geest Industries, and now apartments.

### SH8 SOUTH HOLLAND STEAM MILL, SPALDING
*E bank of river, N of High Bridge.*
*TF 250226*
*Can be seen from public road.*
Four-storey steam flour mill of c1807, later animal feed, with two-storey arch through southern end.   It closed in 1990s and is now apartments.

### SH9 BLACKSMITH'S SHOP, SPALDING
*E bank of river, ½ mile N of town centre.*
*TF 252229*
*Access: View from road.*
Charming early C19 brick workshop on the river bank with a small external yard for fitting iron tyres to wheels. In the wall next to the river is a small hole for work on anchors for coasting and river boats.

### SH10 SPALDING HIGH BRIDGE
*In town centre.*
*TF 248225*
*Access: Public road crosses bridge.*
Single-span stone road bridge over the Welland erected 1838 by the Commissioners of Deeping Fen who were improving the drainage of the area south of the town.

SH10: Spalding High Bridge – CJL

## SH11 RAILWAY FOOTBRIDGES, SPALDING

*About ¼ mile N and S of station.*
TF 244231 and TF 242224
*They are on public footpaths.*
Both built over the railways which converged on Spalding between 1848 and 1882, and extended as the railways arrived from different directions. At TF 242224 is the St John's Road footbridge built in 1860 for the GNR. Of wrought iron and timber it is a very rare and large scale example of the use of wrought iron.

## SH12 SPALDING RAILWAY STATION

*W of town centre.*
TF 242229
*Station still in use.*
The original 1848 Italianate-style block by John Taylor remains of the station built by the GNR, with some extensions, but later buildings erected on the island platforms have gone. It is a larger version of the standard designs used at Bardney and Woodhall Spa.

SH12: Spalding Railway Station – CJL

## SH13 CHATTERTON TOWER, SPALDING

*W of town centre.*
TF 245229
*Can be viewed from public road.*
This water tower of 1955 originally incorporated the 2-storey offices and workshops of the Urban District Council's Water Department.

## SH14 NORTH LEVEL BARRIER BANK, SPALDING TO CROWLAND

*From county boundary at Peakirk to S end of Spalding.*
TF 174068 to TF 242210
*Access: Road runs along top of the bank.*
In 1665 an Act was granted to the Adventurers of Deeping Fen to erect a bank on the east of the R Welland from Peakirk to Spalding, although its origins are probably much earlier. In 1757 the road along the top became the first turnpike road in the Lincolnshire fens.

## SH15 RAILWAY STATION, COWBIT

*3 miles S of Spalding.*
TF 266180
*Access: Private ownership, visible from public road.*
Station, signal box and house on remains of Spalding to March railway of 1867 (originally GN&GEJR).

## SH16 TRINITY BRIDGE, CROWLAND

*In centre of village at junction of 3 main streets.*
TF 239102
*Access: In public street.*
Unique triangular bridge built in 1370 over the

SH15: Cowbit Railway Station – CJL **69**

SH16: Trinity Bridge, Crowland – CJL

R Welland at the point in the centre of the village where it divided into two channels flowing down the middle of the main streets. The river beds were filled-in during C17 after the streams were diverted. It may have replaced an earlier (wooden?) structure of the same configuration as a "porte de Croyland triangulo" is mentioned in 943.

### SH17 MOULTON WINDMILL
*Close to the centre of Moulton village, east of Spalding.*
TF 307240
*Access: From public road, open occasionally.*
This 9-storey brick tower is one of the tallest mills ever built in Britain and claimed to be the largest surviving. The tower is 81ft (24.7m) high to the top of the kerb. It lost its cap and sails in 1895 but retains most of its internal equipment. It was in use in connection with a corn merchant's business until the 1990s and is now being restored by a trust. Featured in "Restoration" on BBC TV in 2003.

### SH18 PENNY HILL MILL, HOLBEACH
*1 mile north of Holbeach centre.*
TF 358267
*Access: view from road.*
Derelict brick tower mill of 1826-27 built on the site of an earlier smock mill, surrounded by a fine range of ancillary buildings. It had ceased working by 1940.

### SH19 SNEATH'S MILL, LONG SUTTON
*Lutton Gowts.*
TF 435243
*Access: View from road.*
This very early tower mill of 1779 at Lutton Gowts is unique in the county in having eight sides, with timber posts at the corners of the brick structure, which give it a close resemblance to a smock mill. It has an all-wooden gearing system. It last worked in the early 1930s, since when it has lost its cap and sails and the interior has slowly deteriorated. It stands on a mill mound so may have superseded an earlier post or smock mill.

SH17: Moulton Windmill - CJL

SH20: Cross Keys Bridge, Sutton Bridge – SES

## SH20 CROSS KEYS BRIDGE, SUTTON BRIDGE

*On main road at east end of the village.*
TF 482210
*Public road crosses bridge.*

This swing bridge was erected over the R Nene in 1894-97 by the M&GNJR, with one carriageway for road traffic and the other for the railway; both used for road traffic since 1963. The steelwork was provided by Handyside & Co. of Derby. It is still opened regularly for shipping going up to Wisbech. It replaced earlier toll bridges of 1830 (by John Rennie) and 1850 (by Robert Stephenson); the toll house of 1830 still remains on the east bank. The 1850 bridge was built as a road bridge and converted to a road/railway bridge in 1866. The bridge is now electrically instead of hydraulically driven. (See SH21)

## SH21 HYDRAULIC TOWER AND ENGINE HOUSE, SUTTON BRIDGE

*On W bank of Nene, S of bridge.*
TF 480209
*Can be seen from a public road.*

This hydraulic accumulator tower, which powered the Cross Keys Bridge (See SH20), is an extremely rare survival. The engine house retains its controls, the two original pumps by Sir W G Armstrong, Whitworth and Co. Ltd., and the accumulators in their timber-clad tower. The boiler house is now empty as the bridge is electrically powered.

## SH22 WAREHOUSE, SUTTON BRIDGE

*On W bank of Nene, N of bridge.*
TF 482211
*Can be viewed from public road.*

Construction of the first bridge and improvements of the R Nene outfall led to the establishment of a village, wharf and warehouses on the west bank from 1830 onwards. The warehouse has been sympathetically converted into apartments.

## SH23 SUTTON BRIDGE DOCK

*Behind W bank of Nene, ½ mile N of bridge.*
TF 482217
*Access: Best viewed from road on opposite (east) bank of river.*

The 13-acre basin constructed behind the west bank of the Nene in 1878-81 had a substantial entrance lock, but the whole dock had poor foundations and parts of its walls collapsed after only one month. The Dock opened 14th May 1881, collapsed 9th June 1881 and was then abandoned. The basin became a golf course, but most of the timber and concrete facing of the basin still remains. In late C20 Port Sutton Bridge was created as a tidal riverside wharf in front of the former Dock.

## SH24 EMBANKMENT, SUTTON BRIDGE

*On A17 road E of R Nene.*
*TF 484210 to TF 503200*
*Access: new road runs along foot of the old Embankment.*

This one and a half mile long bank was built across the old estuary of the R Nene in 1831, after the new channel had been cut and Cross Keys Bridge built, so that the estuary behind the bank could be reclaimed. Since then further land has been reclaimed and the present sea bank is some miles to the north. A road was built along the top of the bank, but the modern A17 now runs on a lower level to the south of the embankment.

## SH25 PORT OF WISBECH ISOLATION HOSPITAL, SUTTON BRIDGE

*On W bank, mile N of bridge.*
*TF 488228*
*Access: View from road.*

Now a Contractor's Yard, within which can be seen the surviving building of this hospital where ships going to and from Wisbech would leave sick seamen.

## SH26 LEADING MARKS, SUTTON BRIDGE

*On E and W banks, 3 miles N of bridge.*
*TF 492258*
*Access: Car park and public footpath on W bank.*

When the new Nene outfall was constructed c1830, two tall leading marks or 'lighthouses' were erected to indicate the entrance to the channel for the benefit of shipping. They were built as lighthouses but never lit. Since then **72** land reclamation has pushed the shore line further out into the Wash.

## SH27 NORTH LEVEL OUTFALL SLUICES, ROAD AND FOOTBRIDGES AT TYDD GOTE, TYDD ST MARY

*2 miles south of Sutton Bridge.*
*TF 468182*
*Access: Public access across sluice.*

Tidal outfall sluices built in 1859 and 1866 for the North Level Commissioners by Robert Stephenson. Site of earlier sluice still visible nearby.

## SH28 CLOUGHS CROSS SLUICE, SUTTON ST EDMUND

*On county boundary, 1 mile north of Parson Drove.*
*TF 368094*
*Access: Public road B1166 crosses over the sluice.*

Unusual double sluice where the North Level Drain and New South Eau combine to form the North Level Main Drain, built in 1855. This is the original structure, though with modern sluice gates.

SH28: Cloughs Cross Sluice, Sutton St Edmund – CJL

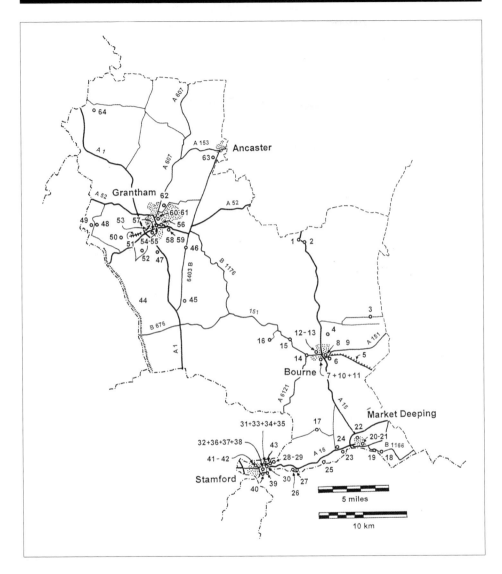

This hilly district in the south-west corner of Lincolnshire includes the towns of Stamford and Grantham. It is an area of rolling limestone hills sloping gently towards the fens on its eastern edge. It is crossed by the Great North Road along its western side, and includes the very early Welland Navigation to Stamford and the Midland-style Grantham Canal to Nottingham. Stamford and Grantham were both on the Great North Road, and when that was supplanted by the GNR in 1852 the character of those towns diverged. Grantham became an important station on the main line to the north but Stamford was avoided by the railway and preserved much of its old character. At Dyke near Bourne is the only remaining smock mill in the county, and there are several watermills though few as large as Newstead Mill at Uffington.

73

SK1: Coaching Inn, Folkingham – CJL

SK3: Pumping Station, Morton Fen – CJL

SK4: Smock Windmill, Dyke,.Bourne – CJL

## SK1 COACHING INN, FOLKINGHAM
*At top end of Market Place.*
TF 072337
*Access: Can be viewed from Market Place.*
The Greyhound inn dominates the sloping market place on the A15 Peterborough-Lincoln road, which in 1756 was one of the first roads in Lincolnshire to be taken over by a turnpike trust.

## SK2 WATER TOWER, FOLKINGHAM
*Beside A15 mile south of Folkingham.*
TF 078325
*Access: view from public road.*
This elegant concrete water tower built in 1983 is a landmark on the southern approach into Folkingham. There are similar towers at Gedney and Whaplode Drove in South Holland.

## SK3 PUMPING STATION, MORTON FEN
*3 miles E of Morton.*
TF 153246
*Access: Visible from public road.*
Built about 1860-70 to house a beam engine. In 1933 that engine was replaced by a twin cylinder Ruston 9XHRC diesel engine that drove a centrifugal pump of 30in (76cm) bore which is a few years older than the engine. Outside the building is the small bed of the temporary engine which had to be installed while the beam engine was being replaced by the diesel.

## SK4 SMOCK WINDMILL, DYKE
*½ mile N of Bourne.*
TF 102226
*Access: Visible from public road.*
The only remaining smock mill in Lincolnshire. The cap, sails and machinery are missing but the shell has been made watertight. Originally built in C18 as a drainage mill in Deeping Fen but moved here in 1845 and converted to corn milling.

## SK5 BOURNE EAU NAVIGATION, BOURNE

*At eastern edge of Bourne.*
TF 104198
*Access: can be seen from public road and paths.*
Head of a navigable branch of the R Glen, the Bourne Eau had been made navigable under an act of 1781. The public wharf is now a car park next to the Anchor PH and there are a few warehouses in this Eastgate area.

## SK6 RAYMOND MAYS' PREMISES, BOURNE

*Eastgate and Spalding Road.*
TF 102199
*Access: View house from Eastgate.    Works is hidden within bus depot on Spalding Road.*
Raymond Mays was the inspiration behind the ERA and BRM motor racing car marques.   His works (which closed in 1981) was situated behind the imposing bay-windowed Eastgate House.

## SK7 BOURNE RAILWAY STATION

*Red Hall, Southgate.*
TF 096196
*Access: Frequently open to the public, especially mornings.*
Red Hall of c1600 was used as passenger sta-tion and station master's house from the arrival of the railway in Bourne in 1861 until it closed in 1959, (though a goods branch remained until 1965). In the grounds a glimpse can be had of the brick goods transhipment shed (See SK 10)

## SK8 BALDOCK'S WATERMILL, BOURNE

*Southgate.*
TF 096199
*Access: Open to the public Saturdays and Sundays, 2 to 4pm all year.*
Restored shell of a C19 corn mill on the Bourne Eau. Now a museum of local life and industries, including a Raymond Mays gallery (British Racing Motors). On the opposite side of the road is an attractive C19 warehouse.

## SK9 SEED WAREHOUSE, BOURNE

*Southgate, opposite Baldock's Mill.*
TF 097200
*Access: View from road.*
Three-storey brick and slate seed warehouse, mid C19, originally owned by Wherry and Sons, agricultural merchants and one of Bourne's leading firms. This listed building was originally part of a larger complex of buildings.

SK9: Seed Warehouse, Southgate, Bourne – CJL

SK10: Railway Goods Shed, at station,
Bourne – CJL

SK11: Railway Goods Shed, east of road,
Bourne – CJL

### SK10 RAILWAY GOODS SHED, BOURNE

*Southgate.*
TF 095195
*Access: Through builder's yard; not visible from road.*
Fine brick warehouse on the site of the M&GNJR railway line, forming part of the Bourne Station complex. (See also SK7)

### SK11 RAILWAY GOODS SHED, BOURNE

*Southgate.*
TF 098195
*Access: On small trading estate.*
This ex-M&GNJR timber goods shed, across the road from the main station, is a rare survival of its kind.

### SK12 PEA WAREHOUSE, BOURNE

*Westgate.*
TF 094203
*Access: View from road.*
A well-restored 4-storey warehouse with prominent lucarn.   Probably mid C18.

### SK13 MALTINGS, BOURNE

*W of centre of Bourne.*
TF 093202
*Access: View from road.*
Late C18 brick maltings rebuilt by John Dove in 1806 after a serious fire and extended in the mid 1800s. Now a printing works.

### SK14 TURNPIKE MILESTONES, BOURNE

*N, W & S of Bourne.*
TF 080198 and elsewhere.
*Access: View from road.*
The roads A15 and A151 from Bourne north to Sleaford, south to Peterborough and west to Colsterworth retain quite a few of their turnpike milestones.

### SK15 LORD WILLOUGHBY'S RAILWAY, EDENHAM

*At north end of village*
TF 058220
*Access: Can be seen from road.*
Lord Willoughby de Eresby of Grimsthorpe Castle had a private railway from Edenham to the GNR at Little Bytham. Originally steam engine operated but later by horse power. Passenger services started in 1857, were intermittent after 1866 and withdrawn 1871. Horse drawn goods service ended in early 1880s. The little weighing office remains beside the road in Edenham. Remains of a never completed northwards extension towards Folkingham can still be seen east of Elsthorpe.

### SK16 DAM, GRIMSTHORPE PARK LAKE, EDENHAM

*In grounds of Grimsthorpe Castle.*
TF 038219
*Access: Public footpath crosses the dam.*
The dam in the park at Grimsthorpe Castle was constructed in 1748 by John Grundy, Jnr. of Spalding. Its scientific design utilising a clay core wall within the dam embankment was well ahead of its time, and was not followed for a century. The public footpath from Edenham village to Swinstead goes across the dam.

*above:* SK18: Low Lock, R Welland,
Deeping St James – NRW
*right:* SK19: Deeping Gate Bridge – NRW

## SK17 BARN, GREATFORD

*On site of Greatford Hall in village centre.*
TF 088118
*Access: Can be viewed from village street.*
A rare early C16 century aisled great barn, the earliest in Lincs but now much restored. It has eight bays of close-studded timber framing over a tall rubble-stone plinth.

## SK18 LOW LOCK, DEEPING ST JAMES

*E end of Deeping St James.*
TF 164089
*It can be reached by a footpath opposite the junction with road B1166.*
At the east end of this village are the remains of a turf-walled pound lock, which consisted of two separate pairs of gates. Both abutments of the top gate remain, now with a guillotine sluice, as well as the north abutment of the lower gate. The lock probably dates from the mid C17 when the R Welland was made navigable through the Deepings and may be the oldest remaining lock in Britain. The adjacent weir is probably the "staunch" built by John Grundy Snr in 1742.

## SK19 DEEPING GATE BRIDGE

*Across Welland, W of Deeping St James.*
TF 151095
*Access: public road over bridge.*
This three-arch stone bridge over the Welland was built in 1651. Near it are the remains of the High Lock on the Welland, which had been made navigable to Market Deeping in the mid C17 and extended to Stamford along the Stamford Canal by 1674.

## SK20 WAREHOUSE, MARKET DEEPING

*E of Market Place.*
TF 141099
*Access: View through archway from road.*
Behind a decorative Gothic-style C19 office is a fine warehouse, now converted to housing. Across the road is the R Welland which was navigable until c1860.

## SK21 TOWN BRIDGE, MARKET DEEPING

*Off Market Place.*
TF 138098
*Access: public road over bridge.*
Three-arch skew bridge built in stone in 1841 to replace an earlier wooden bridge on the county boundary.

## SK22 TURPIKE MILE POSTS, MARKET DEEPING

*N of Parish Church.*
TF 136104 and elsewhere
*Access: beside public road.*
There are still several mile posts on the former turnpike roads to Spalding, Peterborough, Stamford and Lincoln. One near the church indicates the boundary between two districts of the Lincoln Heath to Peterborough trust.

## SK23 MOLECEY'S WATERMILL, WEST DEEPING

*½ mile W of Market Deeping.*
TF 124098
*Can be viewed from public road.*
The original building is C16 with larger C18 additions which are now a private house. The C17 undershot wheel was modified in C19 and is the only Lincolnshire example of Poncelot's improved design. It connects to the great spur wheel, but no other equipment remains.

## SK24 PAPER MILL, WEST DEEPING

*W of Parish Church.*
TF 108086
*Access: view from footpath.*
This is an attractive two-storey watermill next to West Deeping parish church.

## SK25 CANAL LOCK, TALLINGTON

*3 miles W of Market Deeping.*
TF 097079
*Visible to public from adjacent lane.*
Recently discovered remains of turf-walled lock on Stamford Canal.

## SK26 STAMFORD CANAL, UFFINGTON

*W of Uffington Bridge.*
TF 065068
*Access: Public footpath along canal from Uffington Bridge to R Gwash.*
This waterway of the 1670s was created by Stamford Corporation and abandoned c1860, but the dry bed can clearly be followed below Uffington Park as far as Stamford. At TF 050075 stone abutments still support a small wooden bridge over the dried up bed.

## SK27 UFFINGTON BRIDGE

*Barnack Road.*
TF 066069
*A public road across the bridge.*
This late C17 three arch masonry bridge across the R Welland is unusual because of its gradient from south to north across the bridge. It was possibly built to divert the Sewstern Lane drove road away from Uffington Park (See SK44).

## SK28 NEWSTEAD CORN MILL, UFFINGTON

*½ mile E of Stamford.*
TF 047079
*Access: Can be viewed from road.*

This large mill on R Gwash was originally powered by water and later by steam, oil and then electricity. It is a 4-storey stone building of c1840, with a modern extension added 1976.

## SK29 NEWSTEAD TOLLHOUSE, STAMFORD

*Deeping Road, at Newstead.*
TF 047077
*Can be viewed from public road.*

The Deeping to Morcott (Rutland) road via Stamford was turnpiked in 1762. The Newstead Gate tollhouse is in the Tudor style and stayed in use until 1 November 1872 when tolls were abolished on this road.

## SK30 STAMFORD CANAL, STAMFORD

*Town Bridge.*
TF 040073 eastwards
*Parts can be viewed from roads on either bank; from Hudd's Mill eastwards the dried up course can be walked.*

The canal from Stamford to Deeping St James was completed c1670 and can be traced for much of its length along the north side of the valley, including dried up sections east of Hudd's Mill.

## SK31 HUDD'S MILL, STAMFORD

*Off Deeping Road, 400 yards E of St Leonard's Priory.*
TF 042074
*Can be seen from public road.*

This C16 stone watermill still retains its wheel and some equipment. It is at the end of a narrow side lane on the edge of the town.

## SK32 GAS WORKS OFFICE, STAMFORD

*Wharf Road.*
TF 033071
*Access: In public car park.*

In 1826 Stamford had the first gas works in Lincolnshire, and the attractive 2-storey red brick office block still remains next to a car park.

SK32: Gas Works Office, Stamford – NRW

## SK33 BLASHFIELD'S TERRA COTTA WORKS, STAMFORD

*Wharf Road.*
TF 032070
*Access: Can be seen from public road.*

The monumental archway entrance of 1845 to Grant's ironworks, later Blashfield's terra cotta works, was moved a few feet east to its present site in 1937. The arch was originally designed by local architect Bryan Browning. Nothing remains of Blashfield's factory, in operation from 1858 to 1875, but examples of his products can be seen on local buildings including the Scotgate Inn (TF 028071) and No.30 High Street, as well as in Stamford Museum.

## SK34 ALBERT BRIDGE, STAMFORD

*Albert Road, off Wharf Road.*
TF 033069
*A public footbridge still in use.*

Wrought iron footbridge over Welland near Water Street Station. Built 1881 by Everard of Leicester, with Romanesque piers, to replace one of 1863 by Wright of Stamford.

## SK35 WATER STREET STATION, STAMFORD

*Water Street.*
TF 034069
*Can be viewed from public street.*

The architecture of this station of 1855-56 reflects the interest of the Marquis of Exeter, the entrance of whose park is nearby. Designed by William Hurst in a gabled Tudor style, it served a local railway that linked Stamford to

SK35: Water Street Railway Station, Stamford – SES

SK36: Town Bridge, Stamford – SJW

the GNR main line in competition with the MR line to Peterborough. The closed station has been successfully converted to residential and other uses.

### SK36 TOWN BRIDGE, STAMFORD

*High Street, St Martin's.*
TF 030069
*Public bridge still in use.*
This bridge to carry the Great North Road over the R Welland was rebuilt by Lord Exeter in 1848-9, designed by Edward Browning, and the tollhouse at the north east corner still remains. It replaced a medieval bridge of five arches, of which the south arch survives beneath the present south approach. East of the toll house on the north bank are a row of warehouses of c1756.

### SK37 GEORGE HOTEL, ST MARTIN'S, STAMFORD

*High Street, St Martins.*
TF 030068
*Can be viewed from the street.*
This was one of the main coaching inns on the Great North Road. There was an inn here by 1568, and it was enlarged by the Marquis of Exeter in 1785-92.

*below: SK39: Former Pick's Motor Works, Stamford – NRW*
*below right: SK40: Midland Railway Station, Stamford – NRW*

### SK38 MALTINGS, STAMFORD

*St Martin's.*
TF 032068
*Can be viewed from public street.*
Several former maltings remain in the St Martin's area, south of the head of navigation at the Town Bridge. Some have been converted to housing.

### SK39 PICK'S MOTOR WORKS, STAMFORD

*St Martin's, corner of road to Burghley.*
TF 031067
*Access: View from public road.*
This antique shop was previously a petrol filling station, and from 1904 until the mid-1920s it was the Motor Works of John Henry Pick who had made the first motor car to be built in Lincolnshire in 1899.

### SK40 MIDLAND STATION, STAMFORD

*Station Road.*
TF 029066
*This station still in use.*
Built by MR in 1848 west of a tunnel under St Martin's. Designed by Sancton Wood in a Tudor style, with a three-bay arcade, a single-storey booking office and a 2-storey station master's house. Over the waiting room is an octagonal bell-turret. Part is now a bookshop.

**81**

## SK41 KING'S MILL, STAMFORD

*Riverside next to meadows.*
TF 026069
*Can be viewed from public street.*
This two-storey L-shaped water-powered cornmill of c1640 is on an old site on the R Welland. The present building is of coursed rubble walls on an ashlar plinth, and a long granary was added on the north side late in the C18. Two other granaries were added on the south and east sides in the early C19. It has been converted to a recreation centre for children with disabilities.

## SK42 ALL SAINTS BREWERY AND MUSEUM, STAMFORD

*All Saints Street.*
TF 026071
*Open for brewery tours Wed. to Sun. inclusive 11am (1 hour). Groups of 15+.*
*Tel: 01780 752186.*
The C19 All Saints Brewery is preserved, with additional exhibits including the equipment from the estate brewery at Kimbolton Castle. Operates on the vertical principle.

## SK43 STAMFORD MUSEUM

*Broad Street.*
TF 030072
*Open Mon to Sat each week, plus Bank Holiday Mons. From April Sun 1-4*
*For further info ring 01780 766317. e-mail stamford_museum@lincolnshire.gov.uk*
The old industries of Stamford are well repre-sented in this museum operated by Lincoln-shire County Council.

## SK44 SEWSTERN LANE

*From A1 at Long Bennington, leaves Lincolnshire at South Witham*
SK 842432 to SK 902183
*Access: Minor roads or bridleways for most of its length, with a few minor diversions.*
Old drove road from R Trent to R Welland, con-necting with the "Bullock Road" drove road west of Peterborough. For much of its length it forms the county boundary between Lincolnshire and Leicestershire, indicating its great age. Much of its course is followed by minor roads, with diversions where it crosses the Grantham Ca-nal and two later airfields, and it also forms part of the Viking Way long distance footpath. (See also SK27)

## SK45 CHRISTIAN SALVESEN COLD STORE OFFICES, EASTON

*On east side of B6403 1 mile north of junction with A1*
SK 940265
*Access: View from public road*
Attractive single-storey offices of 1973-74 for the vast sheds of the largest Cold Store com-plex in Europe, on the site of the county's last ironstone mine, opened 1958 and closed 1967.

SK46: Woodnook farmstead, Little Ponton – PS

## SK46 WOODNOOK, LITTLE PONTON
*On High Dike (Ermine Street) 1 mile south of*
*Spittlegate roundabout, Grantham*
SK 945326
*Access: View from road*
A complete C19 planned farmstead.

## SK47 GRANGE FARM, LITTLE PONTON
*½ mile west of village, north of start of Grantham*
*Bypass*
SK 918322
*Access: View from road*
A planned farm of 1866, now listed buildings,
built for Christopher Turnor of Stoke Rochford,
one of the largest landowners in C19 Lincolnshire. He built several fine model farms on his
estates in the county.

## SK48 CANAL WORKSHOPS, WOOLSTHORPE BY BELVOIR
*1 mile north-east of Woolsthorpe village, alongside*
*road to "Rutland Arms"*
SK 841350
*Access: Footpath alongside canal.*
Halfway up the Woolsthorpe flight of locks on
the Grantham Canal are the lock keeper's
house, the workshops of the canal company
and the Rutland Arms PH.

## SK49 FLIGHT OF CANAL LOCKS, WOOLSTHORPE BY BELVOIR
*1 mile north-east of Woolsthorpe village, alongside*
*road to "Rutland Arms"*
SK 834350
*Footpath alongside canal, and public road bridge over*
*one lock*
This flight links the top level of the Grantham
Canal to the main level which follows the 150ft
contour around the Vale of Belvoir. The seven

SK47: Grange Farm, Little Ponton – PS

SK48, SK49: Lock on Grantham Canal,
Woolsthorpe by Belvoir – PS

SK51: Cutting on Grantham Canal, Harlaxton – PS

locks took the canal down 59ft (18m). It was opened by 1797 and formally abandoned in 1936 but there are plans for its restoration. The top lock has already been restored.

### SK50 CANAL RESERVOIR, DENTON
*South of Grantham Canal, 1 mile west of Harlaxton Bridge.*
SK 870338
*Access: Visible from public footpath going west from Harlaxton Bridge.*
This supplies the top pound of the Grantham Canal, which was authorised in 1793 and opened at this end in 1797.

### SK51 CANAL CUTTING, HARLAXTON
*½ mile north of Harlaxton village, on road to Barrowby.*
SK 883338
*Access: From Harlaxton Bridge over the canal; towpath beside canal.*
This cutting takes the Grantham Canal through the low ridge separating the Vale of Belvoir from the Witham Valley at Grantham, and is the only substantial engineering work on a Lincolnshire waterway. When this section of the canal was opened by February 1797 the cutting was not wide enough for two full-width boats to pass. Two passing places were made in 1801 and later the whole cutting was widened. The canal was abandoned in 1936 but it is still in water and there are plans afoot for its restoration.

### SK 52 SERVICE RAILWAY, HARLAXTON MANOR
*2 miles west of Grantham*
SK 895322
*Harlaxton Manor is open occasionally.*
Harlaxton Manor is an amazing baroque mansion of the 1830s, and the service wing is to the north-east of the house. It was served by a high level railway that brought coal into the house, through the hill behind, from a lane one and a half miles away.  On open days it is possible to see the house end of the railway.

### SK53 GRANTHAM CANAL
*West of town centre.*
SK 908350 south-westwards
*Access: Site visible from end of Wharf Road.*
This canal was opened in 1797 and formally abandoned in 1936.  The terminus basin and much of the eastern end have been filled in and disappeared but there are active plans for the restoration of the canal westwards from the modern Grantham bypass. (See SK 48 to 51).

## SK54 RAILWAY STATION, GRANTHAM

*South-west of town centre*
SK 913351
*Access: Station is still open for traffic.*

Built by GNR in 1852 on the main line from London to the north, and subsequently enlarged as other GNR branches converged on Grantham. This was the least easy section of the GNR to construct. The line went west of Grantham to avoid Lord Brownlow's park at Belton House though this necessitated tunnels to the north and south of Grantham, at Peascliffe and Stoke.

## SK55 BROWNLOW CARRIAGE WORKS, GRANTHAM

*Wharf Road, near Station approach*
SK 912353
*Access: Now Jewson's commercial premises, open during business hours.*

This was Richard J. Boyall's Brownlow Carriage, Harness and "Steam Wheel" Works from c1860 to 1890. Boyalls manufactured a wide range of horse drawn vehicles and associated gear including artillery wheels for Ordnance Manufacturers at home and abroad. Traces remain of their wide range of workshops, forges and storage sheds, particularly their showroom building which is still extant in a fine state of repair and restoration.

## SK56 SPITTLEGATE IRONWORKS, GRANTHAM

*Spring Hill, off London Road, south of town centre.*
SK 916351
*Access: can be seen from road.*

In Victorian and Edwardian times Richard Hornsby & Sons was one of the great engineering firms of Lincolnshire and did much to develop the first successful diesel engine. In 1918 they amalgamated with Rustons of Lincoln and the works in Grantham were later closed. A few remaining workshops are visible from the top of Spring Hill (off London Road) and the top of Station Road east near St Johns Church.

## SK57 BMARC FACTORY, GRANTHAM

*Springfield Road.*
SK 910346
*Access: Regular access to front of site*

The British Manufacturing and Research Co. was formed by the British Government and Hispano-Suiza during the 1930s re-armament programme and this large site produced many thousands of weapons, mainly cannon, under various owners until closure in the 1990s.

## SK58 MALTINGS, GRANTHAM

*Off A52 as it crosses R Witham on way to Boston, at bottom of hill.*
SK 921350
*Access: Can be viewed from road.*

The many maltings in Grantham have been replaced by a single large modern building, but a few of the old buildings remain including this one. Other surviving examples are next to the railway at SK 914350 and SK 903370.

## SK59 SPITTLEGATE WATERMILL (SWALLOW'S MILL), GRANTHAM

*Off A52 as it crosses R Witham on way to Boston, at bottom of hill.*
SK 922349
*Access: Can be seen from road*

This corn mill dates from the late C18 or early C19, but new machinery was installed in 1886 and part remains although the building is now private housing.

## SK60 GEORGE HOTEL, GRANTHAM

*On west side of High Street, in town centre.*
SK 913357
*Access: now a shopping mall.*

In Georgian times Grantham was one of the main stops on the Great North Road, and this led to the reconstruction of the George in 1780 as one of the main coaching inns on the road. In the 1990s it closed and was converted to a shopping centre.

SK55: Brownlow Carriage Works, Grantham – PS

**85**

## SK61 ANGEL AND ROYAL HOTEL, GRANTHAM

*At northern end of town centre, on former Great North Road*
SK 913359
*Access: Hotel open for business during commercial hours*
The Angel and Royal was built in the C15/C16 and occupied a prime position on the Great North Road being one day's journey from London. In addition to its prestigious frontage it has a typical coach archway and, through its yard flanked by many outbuildings, former stabling and other service buildings.

## SK62 LONDONTHORPE WATERMILL, MANTHORPE

*½ mile north of Grantham*
SK 924380
*Access: At end of minor road on east side of Witham.*
This C19 corn mill last worked in 1963 but the eastern half of the brick building still contains 3 pairs of stones and the wooden high breast shot wheel (dia. 16ft or 4.9m) made by Wakes and Lamb of Newark in 1914.

## SK63 WILSFORD QUARRIES

*On west side of B6403, ½ mile south of Ancaster.*
SK 979427
*Access: No public access, but can be seen from the road access*
Ancaster Limestone has been quarried in this area since medieval times and can be seen in many local churches and other important buildings. This quarry opened in the early 1900s but is now closed. Between here and Oasby are other quarries, worked until the 1940s.

## SK64 WATERMILL, CLAYPOLE

*South of village*
SK 843480
*Access: At end of minor road.*
This mill was processing flax by 1797 but had reverted to a corn mill by 1872. It is away from the main village and in the Napoleonic period had a small colony of cottages and workshops around it. It ceased working in 1947 and is now a grain store in a bad state of preservation. The mill race and tail race have since been filled in and grassed over.

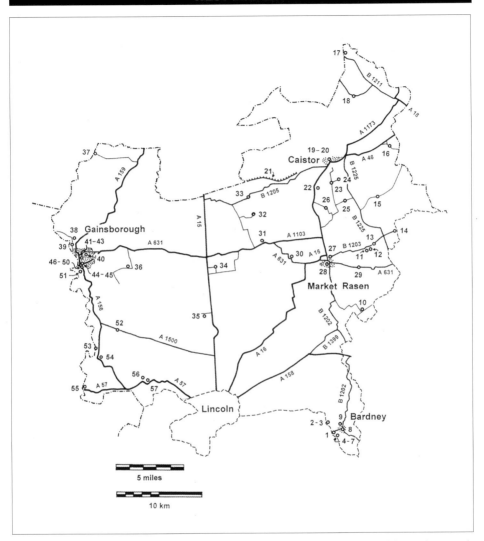

This district lies north of Lincoln on the western side of Lincolnshire and its main town is Gainsborough, home of the world-renowned firm of Marshall & Sons for over a century. Gainsborough was for long an important port on the lower Trent, before becoming an engineering town dependent on Marshall's, and the Fossdyke Canal and R Ancholme were navigations within the District. Most of the District is rural, and includes the small towns of Caistor and Market Rasen as well as the northern dormitories of Lincoln and many rural villages. Within the district are several planned farms, and the remains of watermills at Tealby in the eastern part of the district. There is a lot of industrial interest in Bardney including the Witham navigation, the former railway along the river bank, and the former sugar beet factory that has been closed since 2001.

**87**

WL1: Road Bridge, Bardney – NRW

## WL1 ROAD BRIDGE, BARDNEY
*At west end of village, over the R Witham.*
TF 112691
*Access: From road or from river banks.*
Built in 1893 to replace a ferry at this point over the R Witham. The house on the west bank of the river here is the former ferry cottage. Funded by a local business man with contributions from GNR and Lindsey County Council.

## WL2 BARDNEY RAILWAY BRIDGE
*On east bank of Witham, next to lock, ½ mile north of road bridge.*
TF 103700
*Access: public footpath along river bank.*
This steel railway bridge over the R Witham

near Bardney lock was built in 1860 to replace the original timber bridge of 1848, which was the longest timber bridge to be built on this GNR line. It spanned 729yds (666.6m), and the original designer's scale model can be seen in the National Railway Museum at York.

## WL3 BARDNEY LOCK
*On R Witham about ½ mile north of road bridge.*
TF 103700
*Access: by public footpath on bank of river or by track off B1190 road.*
Rebuilt 1865 to replace the original lock of c1770. It has unusual curved gates like those at Antons Gowt and Lincoln.

WL2: Railway Bridge, Bardney – PS

## WL4 BARDNEY SUGAR BEET FACTORY

*At west end of village, south of road bridge over Witham.*
TF 113688
*Access: View from public road.*

Erected 1927 between the GNR Loop Line and the R Witham as part of a government scheme to reduce dependence on imported cane sugar. Its raw material was delivered by road, rail, water and the Nocton Estate Light Railway. An overhead gantry across the R Witham, which also unloaded barges, served the latter. It finally ceased beet processing in February 2001, the last of its type in the county. Liquid sugar and treacle were still being produced on the site in 2003.

## WL5 GOODS SHED, BARDNEY

*At west end of village, on north side of main street.*
TF 113691
*Access: View from road.*

The GNR Loop Line from Peterborough to Lincoln came through Bardney in 1848, and a branch line later went to Louth. The station closed in the early 1970s and most of the buildings were demolished in 1993; the surviving goods shed was converted into a dwelling during 2002/3.

## WL6 GAS HOUSE, BARDNEY

*West end of village, north of road to the east of the road bridge.*
TF 112691
*Access: View from road.*

The Gas House was built about 1860 for "The Bardney Gas Light and Coke Company" which ceased trading during the 1920s when electricity was introduced into the village.

## WL7 MORRELL'S FACTORY, BARDNEY

*North of Station Road, west end of village next to road bridge over Witham.*
TF 113692
*Access: View from public road or river bank.*

The large building next to the former railway track was originally a store for Mr Sharpe who produced peas and potatoes. During the mid 1930s the building was taken over by Fosters Canning Co., later to become Morrells, who canned ham, peas, vegetables and Red Heart dog food here until the late 1980s. This façade contains an original VR post box.

## WL8 CO-OPERATIVE SHOP NO.11, BARDNEY

*Queen Street, opposite Fish Shop.*
TF 121696
*Access: View from public road.*

The Lincoln Co-op opened this as Store No.11 in 1896 and it had its own bakery. A new Co-op has been opened in Bardney and during 2002 the original Co-op was converted to a private house.

## WL9 BARDNEY WATER TOWER

*Down Abbey Road, north of the village.*
TF 117703
*Access: View from public road.*

Bardney Water Tower was built about 1903 and was fed from boreholes near the tower. These boreholes supplied water to the village until 1938 after which a new piped mains water supply was pumped from Welton.

## WL10 MANOR FARM, EAST TORRINGTON

*Adjacent to East Torrington Parish Church.*
TF 147834
*Access: No public access; view from road.*

A planned Victorian farmstead of the period 1855 to 1865, built by Christopher Turnor. The range of buildings clearly indicates the uses needed on a farm at the time that the process was becoming industrialised, including crew yards, barn, granary, loose boxes, stables, smithy and coach house.

## WL11 TEALBY THORPE WATERMILL

*East of ford at Tealby Thorpe, 1 mile south-west of Tealby village.*
TF 150900
*Access: View from road.*

This is a corn mill of 1790 on the R Rase and it still retains its machinery. A two-storey brick extension over the river contains the breast shot wheel.

WL7: Morrell's Factory, Bardney – NRW

WL12: Tyson's Watermill, Tealby – NRW

## WL12 TEALBY WATERMILL

*Thorpe Lane, Tealby, south-west of village.*
TF 155903
*Access: Alongside the public road, no public access.*
Tysons Mill, built about 1790, was powered by a breastshot wheel, the site of which can be seen alongside the road. The wheel was later replaced by a turbine.

## WL13 LOWER MILL, TEALBY

*South of Papermill Lane, ¼ mile east of the village.*
TF 163910
*Access: No public access but can be seen from the road.   Note: Take great care, the road is very narrow, with narrow verges for pedestrians.*
Ruins of a papermill can be seen among the trees below Papermill Lane. It was built about 1791 and believed to have worked up to 1836 when converted to two cottages and last inhabited about 1940. Other papermills used to exist along this stretch of the R Rase but have left no visible remains.

## WL14 MANOR FARM, KIRMOND LE MIRE

*In centre of village, on north side of B1203.*
TF 188927
*Access: View from road; no public access.*
This Victorian High Farm was built by Christopher Turnor in 1868 and the farmstead is listed. In the village he also built three sets of farm cottages, the school, and rebuilt the Parish Church in 1847. Manor Farm is probably the best example of its type in the county, catering for all of the farm activities on an industrial scale and equipped to use the steam power of a stationary portable engine driving line shafting through the centre of the main complex.

## WL15 THORESWAY WATERWHEEL

*Alongside the road in the centre of the village.*
TF 165966
*Access: View building from road; no public access.*
This overshot wheel in its own roadside building was erected c1818 to provide power for a threshing machine and other implements in a farm building on the other side of the road. Pins around the rim of the wheel operated a cog and axle which transferred the power under the road. The wheel remains but the overhead leet which brought water to it from a pond on the hillside has gone.

WL14: Manor Farm, Kirmond le Mire – SES

WL15: Waterwheel, Thoresway – SES

## WL16 GRANGE FARM, SWALLOW

*North side of A46, ¼ mile west of the village cross roads.*

TA 168028

*Access: View from road. Caution, this road is very busy. Park at end of old road.*

One of a number of farms established on the Lincolnshire Wolds by the Earl of Yarborough, this one in 1830. A feature of these farms, located as they are on the higher parts of the waterless chalk Lincolnshire Wolds, was the horse powered water pump, in a building similar in appearance to a horse engine house, an example of which can be seen here.

## WL17 RAILWAY STATION, BROCKLESBY

*Alongside the B1121, between Brocklesby and Ulceby.*

TA 119136

*Access: View from road, station now closed.*

Opened in 1848 on the main line of the MSLR near the home of the Earl of Yarborough, Chairman of the Company. As such this station by Weightman and Hadfield has fine architectural detailing in Jacobean style.

## WL18 BOUNDARY FARM, GREAT LIMBER

*At west end of the village.*

TA 128086

*Access: View from road.*

This late C18 planned or model farm is part of the Brocklesby estate of the Earls of Yarborough. It includes stables, barn, crew yard and cart sheds laid out in the traditional E shape.

## WL19 FORMER FIRE STATION, CAISTOR

*Horsemarket, alongside the road south of town centre.*

TA 110010

*Access: View from street.*

At the end of Horsemarket is a pair of doors giving access to a tunnel beneath Nettleton Road. This is the former Fire Station of 1869.

## WL20 NAVIGATION LANE, CAISTOR

*Runs due west from Caistor.*

TA 110010

*Access: Public road and public footpath.*

This lane runs westwards from the town and was built in 1800 to link the town with the proposed terminal basin of the Caistor Canal. However, the canal reached only as far as Moortown so the lane was never used for its original purpose.

## WL21 CAISTOR CANAL, SOUTH KELSEY

*Moortown and South Kelsey.*

TF 071992 to TF 011990

*Access: Can be seen from various public roads.*

The canal designed by William Jessop passes through the parish from its junction with the Ancholme to its former terminal basin at Moortown. It was never extended to Caistor, presumably because of difficult (ie very sandy) ground conditions between Moortown and Caistor. Opened c1795 it was four miles long with six locks lifting boats some 42 feet from the Ancholme. It closed in 1855. Near to the junction with the Ancholme is **Beck End Lock**, (TF 011990). The route, now a drainage channel, and the site of the **wharf** can be seen at

South Kelsey, (TF 043989), to the east of the road bridge. At Moortown a house in the north west of the cross roads, (TF 071992) was probably built originally as a warehouse at the site of the **terminal basin**.

### WL22 RAILWAY STATION AND SIGNAL BOX, HOLTON LE MOOR
*Alongside the A46, east of the village.*
TF 092975
*Access: View from road.*
The original station buildings and signal box on this line, opened in 1848, are typical of those found at village stations on the several MSLR lines in north Lincolnshire. The line is still open but the station (now a private house) was closed for goods on 15th June 1964 and passengers on 1st November 1965.

### WL23 IRONSTONE MINES, NETTLETON
*East and west of Nettleton Top about 1 mile south of the village.*
TF 110981, TF 114981, TF 125983
*Access: View from road.*
There were two underground Ironstone Mines here. **Nettleton Top Mine**, 1928-59, and **Nettleton Bottom Mine**, 1957-68. On the road at Nettleton Top (TF 114981), Top Mine is beneath your feet. Its entrance was on the hillside to the west (TF 110981), where surviving buildings can be seen. From here an aerial ropeway carried stone to Holton le Moor sidings from where it was sent to Scunthorpe. The ropeway was replaced by the existing road in 1959. The rough ground in the field to the west of the road is the result of pit falls. The sides of the valley to the east were worked on the surface where the stone outcropped. A concrete road heading off to the east is the remains of the surface route to Bottom Mine. Nettleton Bottom valley can be reached along the Viking Way footpath. Here are the adits to Bottom Mine (TF 124983), and the embankment which carried the rails over the valley.

### WL24 CHALK QUARRY, NETTLETON
*West of Caistor High Street, 2 miles south of Caistor.*
TF 125983
*Access: View from Viking Way long distance footpath, 1 mile south of village.*
This is best seen from Nettleton Top. It was opened in 1960 to supply chalk for use in Scunthorpe steelworks. Large dumper trucks carried the stone to Holton le Moor sidings from

where it was sent to Scunthorpe by rail. This traffic ceased in 1970.

### WL25 CIVIL AVIATION AUTHORITY RADAR MAST, NORMANBY LE WOLD
*¾ of a mile north east of the village, on the north side of a minor road.*
TF 125962
*Access: View from public road.*
Built in the mid-1980s, this mast helps to police the skies for aircraft travelling across northern England

### WL26 IRONSTONE MINE MANAGER'S HOUSE, CLAXBY
*Alongside a minor road, 1 mile north of the village.*
TF 106956
*Access: View from road.*
The Claxby Ironstone Mine was in operation from 1868 to 1885, high on the hillside to the north of Claxby. Its remains can still be seen there today although they are not accessible to the public. This house, alongside the minor road north of the village, was built originally for the mine manager. Two terraces of nearby miners cottages were demolished in 1972/3.

### WL27 CHURCH MILL, MARKET RASEN
*George Street, to the north of the parish church.*
TF 107894
*Access: View from road.*
The five-storey mill has now been converted into flats. It was built about 1830 as the ware-

WL22: Railway Station and Signal Box, Holton le Moor – NRW

house for the proposed terminal basin of a canal from Bishopbridge to Market Rasen (See WL31), abandoned with the coming of the railway to the town. Converted to a mill, it was originally powered by an undershot wheel replaced by an Armfield Turbine in 1930 which ran until 1959.

## WL28 RAILWAY STATION, MARKET RASEN

*Off Chapel Street.*
TF 108888
*Access: Railway Station open to the public.*
The imposing single-storey railway station on this MSLR branch line, opened in 1848, originally had an all-over timber roof.  The line and station are still open but the only building now in use for passengers is a timber waiting room on the up platform, itself a rare survival on the modern railway.

## WL29 TURNPIKE MILE POSTS, MARKET RASEN

*Along the A631 Louth to Bawtry road.*
TF 117888, TF 134885, TF 149885, TF 165883, TF 181887
*Access: Alongside public road.*
There are still many stone mileposts along this stretch of the road between Louth and Bawtry, which was taken over by a turnpike trust in 1765.

WL29: Turnpike Milestone,
Market Rasen – KR

**93**

WL30: Packhorse Bridge, West Rasen – SES

## WL30 PACKHORSE BRIDGE, WEST RASEN
*North side of A631, in the centre of the village.*
TF 063983
*Access: Public footpath over.*
An attractive stone bridge, built of local iron-stone, and thought to have been built by a Bishop of Lincoln in 1310. Three nearly equal spans with ribbed arches and low parapets so as not to foul the loads carried by packhorses. Recently refurbished by Lincolnshire County Council.

## WL31 HEAD OF ANCHOLME NAVIGATION, BISHOPSBRIDGE
*North side of A631, park in lay-by by the public house.*
TF 032911
*Access: View from road and footpaths.*
In 1826 the R Ancholme Navigation was extended to this point 10 miles above Brigg and a small community developed, with wharves, warehouses, houses and a chapel. The four-storey building surviving on the west bank was a steam mill. Opposite it, on the other bank, is the former Manager's House. Proposals to extend the waterway to Market Rasen or to link it **94** with the R Witham came to nothing (See WL27).

## WL32 HARLAM HILL LOCK, BISHOP NORTON
*2 miles east of Snitterby, On the towpath of the R Ancholme.*
TF 020944
*Access: Nearest access to towpath from public road ½ mile to the north.*
This is the highest lock on the R Ancholme Navigation. The upper gate is a guillotine but the lower gate has the original 1827 casings on the winch paddle. The iron balance beams, of an unusual slender design, may also be original.

## WL33 ROAD BRIDGE, WAREHOUSE AND INN, BRANDY WHARF
*On B1205 between Waddingham and South Kelsey.*
TF 015970
*Access: Along the public road.*
This cast iron bridge on stone abutments was built in 1831 across the Ancholme Navigation. It was designed by Sir John Rennie and the ironwork was by the Butterley Company. It was strengthened in 1988 by the insertion of steel beams between the cast iron beams which had been "sprung" (ie deformed) by overloading. The adjacent warehouse and Anchor PH are

of around the same date. This is now the limit for larger vessels using the Ancholme.

## WL34 OWMBY CLIFF FARM, CAENBY CORNER

*East of A15, 1½ miles south of Caenby Corner.*
SK 974870
*Access: View from public footpath passing site.*

Great changes came about in agriculture during the 1960s and this good example of the large-scale architecture of 'agribusiness' can be seen from the nearby A15 road.

## WL35 INGHAM WEATHER RADAR

*¾ mile east of village.*
SK 961830
*Access: Can be seen from public road.*

Erected in the mid 1980s, it is one of a network of radar stations throughout the British Isles feeding rainfall data to the Meteorological Office for weather forecasting.

## WL36 HEAPHAM WINDMILL

*West of Heapham village, on the road to Gainsborough.*
SK 873887
*Access: Open on selected weekends during the summer. Alongside the public road.*

This four-sailed brick tower mill was built in 1876. It worked until 1956 when it lost its sails in a storm. Restored to working order by its owner in 1996, it is now open to the public. On the site a Ruston and Hornsby 22 bhp engine can also be seen, installed here in 1931.

## WL37 WHARF TALLY HOUSE, SUSWORTH

*On east side of village street, alongside the R Trent.*
SE 835022
*Access: Alongside the public road.*

A small brick building alongside the road facing the R Trent is said to be the Tally House for the wharf which once was by the river here. In the C18 and C19 all of the riverside communities depended for their transport needs on the river, and boats would tie up at many places. Susworth wharf also served the large village of Scotter, three miles to the east.

## WL38 WINDMILL, MORTON (Near Gainsborough)

*North end of village.*
SK 811921
*Access: View from road.*

Built 1820 but disused by 1899. For many years it stood as part of the premises of the Gainsborough Laundry. By 1993 the tower was a ruin with no internal floors or roof and it was converted into an office, including the erection of a traditional ogee cap.

## WL39 WAREHOUSES, MORTON (Near Gainsborough)

*Off Front Street.*
SK 806916
*Access: Public footpath alongside river passes the site.*

This was a small landing place on the bank of the Trent. Part of the row of former warehouses remains on the former Morton Wharf.

## WL40 WATER TOWER, GAINSBOROUGH

*Cox's Hill, on crest of ridge E of town centre.*
SK 821900
*Access: View from road.*

This tower of 1897 is an elaborate structure complete with a memorial tablet giving full details. It provided a water supply to the upper part of Gainsborough which could not be served by the adjacent service reservoirs. It was superseded by the Ash Grove water tower.

WL36: Heapham Windmill – KR

WL41:
Oil Pumps,
Gainsborough –
SES

## WL41 OIL PUMPS, GAINSBOROUGH

*Alongside Gainsborough Central Station.*
SK 819898
*Access: View from road and footpaths.*

An extensive oilfield in north Nottinghamshire was developed during the Second World War and later extended into north west Lincolnshire. There were several wells in and around Gainsborough. The last of these can be seen here, marked by a row of four of the traditional pumps known a 'nodding donkeys'.

## WL42 BRITANNIA IRONWORKS, GAINSBOROUGH

*Beaumont Street.*
SK 818898
*Access: Most of the site is a retail park to be opened in 2005.*

After c1860 the ironworks of William Marshall and Sons came to dominate this town. Although now much reduced in size it is still the best surviving example of a Victorian engineering works left in Lincolnshire. English Heritage have declared it to be nationally significant and an exemplar of the evolution of the engineering works as a type. In 2004 much of the site was redeveloped as a retail park.

## WL43 WHITTON'S MILL, GAINSBOROUGH

*Bridge Street.*
SK 814896
*Access: View from road and riverside path.*

Built in 1936 to the design of Thomas Tatam, to mill flour brought to the site by the R Trent. This is the most prominent waterside building in the town. Milling ceased in 1995 and following two fires which caused much damage, it has been converted into flats.

## WL44 MALTINGS, GAINSBOROUGH

*Bridge Street.*
SK 814893
*Access: Public access to either side.*

These are the former Sandars Maltings first established here between Bridge Street and the R Trent in the 1790s. This large and complex site developed in six phases of building up to the 1840s. Partial demolition took place in 1996. What is seen today is an L-shaped building with a late C18 front to the river, widened and re-roofed c1840. It has an C18 kiln at its south end. The return wing is a malting of 1840.

## WL45 GAINSBOROUGH, PLANNED STREETS

*High Street and Britannia Terrace.*
SK 818893
*Access: Alongside public roads.*

These streets of brick Victorian houses were built for the workers in the adjacent Britannia Works of William Marshall and Sons.

WL42: Britannia Ironworks, Gainsborough – SES

## WL46 WAREHOUSES, GAINSBOROUGH
*Bridge Street.*
SK 814892 northwards
*Access: Public access to either side.*
Several warehouses, maltings and wharves of C18 and C19 survive along Bridge Street on the east bank of the R Trent, but those between Chapel Staithe and the end of Lord Street have been demolished.

## WL47 TRENT BRIDGE, GAINSBOROUGH
*Carries A631 over the R Trent.*
SK 814892
*Access: A public road.*
A fine three-span ashlar masonry bridge of 1790 by William Weston – his last work in England before emigrating to the USA where he became well known as a canal engineer. Its stone balustrades were replaced by railings when the cantilevered footpaths were added in 1964. The bridge across the Trent was freed from tolls on 31st March 1932 but still has the original toll houses at its east end. Both of two-storeys, they were at one time a single house connected by a tunnel under the roadway and were restored in 2002.

## WL48 MARSHALL'S ELECTRICITY WORKS, GAINSBOROUGH
*On Lea Road, south of the Trent Bridge.*
SK 814890
*Access: Alongside the public road.*
In 1918 Marshalls decided that their electricity supply should be provided from their own power station by the R Trent. The building housed two 1500kw steam driven generators. It was closed in 1955.

## WL49 SPILLERS MILL, GAINSBOROUGH
*Carr Lane.*
SK 812884
*Access: Can be seen from Trent Bridge.*
This seven-storey mill complex was built between 1958 and 1962. Sited here because this was the highest point on the R Trent served by sea going ships. It still produces flour today.

## WL50 EDLINGTON'S WORKS, GAINSBOROUGH
*Lea Road.*
SK 816887
*Access: View exterior from public road.*
One of the town's mid C19 engineering factories. This works produced agricultural machinery for the local market and further afield.

## WL51 LEA ROAD STATION, GAINSBOROUGH
*Lea Road.*
SK 819883
*Access: A public station and alongside the public road.*
The GNR used the MSLR station (buildings

WL47: Trent Bridge, Gainsborough – SES

**97**

WL52: GNR Railway Station and Signal Box, Stow Park – NRW

demolished 1974) from 1848 until they built the Lea Road Station in 1867. The main brick building, now a garden centre, is at the foot of the embankment with the platforms and shelters at a higher level behind. Waiting rooms were added behind the shelters in 1882 with the formation of the GN&GEJR. The shelters were reduced from five bays to three in 1981.

### WL52 RAILWAY STATION AND SIGNAL BOX, STOW PARK
*On A1500 1 mile east of Marton.*
SK 856815
*Access: Alongside the public road.*
A rare grouping on the modern railway of station buildings, signal box, traditional level crossing gates and semaphore signals. Now listed. The stone station was built when the line opened in 1849. The signal box, of typical GNR style, followed in the 1880s and the interior is intact.

### WL53 RAILWAY BRIDGE AND VIADUCT, TORKSEY
*At the north end of the village, west of the A156.*
SK 835791
*Access: Can be seen from the public road. Part of a Sustrans proposal which may see its future use for cyclists and pedestrians.*
Designed by John Fowler and opened in 1850 to carry the MSLR across the R Trent. This is the second oldest girder bridge of its type left in the world. A pioneering piece of engineering design in two respects. It used wrought iron box-girders which were structurally continuous over the central pier. The Commissioners for Railways initially refused to sanction its opening and a furious debate took place before the Commissioners backed down. It was strengthened in 1897 by the insertion of a central steel girder. The line closed in 1959 but was reopened in 1966 for goods trains to Torksey from Sykes Junction to serve an oil terminal alongside the viaduct. The depot closed and trains finally stopped running in 1988.

### WL54 TIDE LOCK, TORKSEY
*Alongside the A156 to the south of the village.*
SK 838780
*Access: Alongside the public road.*
The only lock on the Fossdyke Navigation is here where the latter joins the tidal Trent. The Fossdyke dates from Roman times but deteriorated until restored in 1744. The lock (c1810?) has four sets of doors opened by capstans because at high tide the water levels in the Trent can exceed those in the canal.

WL54: Tidal Lock, Fossdyke Navigation, Torksey – NRW

WL55: Dunham Aqueduct, Newton on Trent – SES

## WL55 DUNHAM TOLLBRIDGE, AQUEDUCT AND FORMER DOCK

*Over R Trent at Newton on Trent.*
SK 820745
*Access: Public road.*

A toll-bridge was first built here in 1832, replacing a ferry on the turnpike road from Lincoln to the Great North Road. That was a bowstring bridge designed by George Leather. The present toll-bridge replaced the original in 1979. The aqueduct alongside it is of 1910/11 and carries the water pipeline from Elkseley to Lincoln in a clear span of 262ft (80m). On the north side of the bridge a towpath bridge marks the entrance to a small dock off the R Trent which once served the needs of the nearby villages.

## WL56 RAILWAY STATION AND SIGNAL BOX, SAXILBY

*In the centre of the village.*
SK 892753
*Access: Station still open for passengers.*

This stone built station was built by the GNR in 1849. The Signal Box, protecting a public road to the south, replaced an earlier one within the station limits in 1922. It has a strong LNER style.

## WL57 CANAL FOOTBRIDGE, SAXILBY

*Bridge Street.*
SK 895752
*Access: Open for public use, alongside the public road.*

This footbridge was built for the GNR in 1883 for the Lincoln Road level crossing at Newark. That level crossing was replaced by a bridge in 1936 and this footbridge was moved and rebuilt at Claypole to carry a public footpath over the then recently widened East Coast Main Line. In 1987 work on electrifying the line meant that it was again surplus and it was re-erected here in Saxilby as part of enhancement works alongside the Fossdyke Navigation. It is located on the abutments of an earlier swing bridge, removed in 1937 when the present village by-pass opened.

WL56: GNR Signal Box, Saxilby - NRW

**99**

Armstrong, M E (Ed.), — *An Industrial Island: A History of Scunthorpe,* Scunthorpe Borough Museum and Art Gallery, Scunthorpe 1981

Beckwith, I S, — *The Industrial Archaeology of Gainsborough,* 1968

Beckwith, I S (Ed.), — *The Louth Riverhead,* 1976

Bennett, S and Bennett, N, — *An Historical Atlas of Lincolnshire,* Hull University Press 1993

Birch, N C, — *The Waterways and Railways of Lincoln and the lower Witham,* 1968

Birch, N C, — *Stamford: An Industrial History,* 1972

Blake, R, Hodgson, M and Taylor, W, — *The Airfields of Lincolnshire since 1912,* Midland Counties Publications, Leicester 1984

Boyes, J and Russell, R. — *The Canals of Eastern England,* David and Charles, Newton Abbot 1977

Clarke, R H, — *Steam Engine Builders of Lincolnshire,* Goose & Son, Norwich 1955, reprinted by Society for Lincolnshire History and Archaeology, Lincoln 1998

Colsell, L (Ed.), Brooks, R and Longdon, M, — *Lincolnshire Built Engines,* Lincolnshire County Council Recreational Services-Museums, Lincoln 1986

Cove-Smith, C, — *The Grantham Canal Today,* Mitchell, Nottingham 1974

Dobinson, C, — *Twentieth Century Fortifications in England,* Council for British Archaeology 1996

Dolman, P, — *Lincolnshire Windmills – A contemporary survey,* Lincolnshire County Council, Department of Recreational Services, Lincoln 1986

Dow, G, — *Great Central,* 1959-65

Hadfield, C, — *The Canals of the East Midlands,* David & Charles, Newton Abbot 1970

Hancock, T, — *Bomber County,* Vols. 1 & 2, Lincolnshire County Council Recreational Services Department-Libraries 1978 & 1985

Hills, R L, — *The Drainage of the Fens,* 2003

Holm, S A, — *Brick and Tile Making in South Humberside,* 1976

Jones, M J, Stocker, D and Vince, A, — *The City by the Pool,* Oxbow Books Oxford 2003

Judson, P and Lester, C, — *Twentieth Century – What Heritage?,* Heritage Trust of Lincolnshire, Sleaford 2001

Lane, M R, — *The Story of the Britannia Iron Works, Gainsborough,* Quiller Press, London 1993

Lane, M R, — *The Story of the Wellington Foundry, Lincoln,* Unicorn Press, London 1997

Lewis, M J T and Wright, N R, — *Boston as a Port,* 1974

Mills, D R (Ed.), — *Twentieth Century Lincolnshire,* History of Lincolnshire Committee for the Society for Lincolnshire History and Archaeology, Lincoln 1989

Newman, B, — *One hundred years of good company,* 1957

| Osborne, M, | *20th Century Defences in Britain: Lincolnshire,* Brassey's, London 1997 |
|---|---|
| Page, C J, | *History of the Ancholme Navigation,* 1969 |
| Page, C J, | *Sleaford – An Industrial History,* 1974 |
| Pawley, S, | *Sleaford and the Slea,* Griffin, Penkridge 1990 |
| Pointer, M, | *Hornsby's of Grantham 1815-1918*, 1976 |
| Robinson, P, | *Lincoln's Excavators – The Ruston Years 1875-1930*, 2003 |
| Ruddock, J G and Pearson, R E, | *The Railway History of Lincoln*, J. G. Ruddock and Partners, Lincoln 1974 |
| Russell, R, | *Lost Canals of England and Wales*, David and Charles, Newton Abbot 1971 |
| Squires, S,E, | *The Lost Railways of Lincolnshire*, Castlemead, Ware 1988 |
| Walshaw, G R and Behrendt, C A R, | *The History of Appleby-Frodingham*, Appleby-Frodingham Steel Co., Scunthorpe, 1950 |
| Wright, N R, | *Lincolnshire Towns and Industry 1700-1914*, History of Lincolnshire Committee for the Society for Lincolnshire History and Archaeology, Lincoln 1982 |
| Wright, N R, | *Sutton Bridge and Long Sutton, Lincolnshire – An Industrial History*, Society for Lincolnshire History and Archaeology, Lincoln, 1996 |
| Wrottesley, J, | *The Great Northern Railway*, Batsford, London 1979-81 |

## MUSEUMS AND PLACES TO VISIT

Aircraft Control Tower, East Kirkby 01790 763207

All Saints Brewery and Museum, Stamford 01780 752186

Ayscoughfee Hall Museum, Spalding 01775 725468

Anderby Drainage Engine, Anderby Creek 01754 871594 or 01754 872599

Battle of Britain Memorial Flight, Coningsby 01526 344041

Bourne Museum, Baldocks Mill, Bourne

Church Farm Museum, Skegness 01754 766658

Cogglesford Watermill, Sleaford 01529 414294

Cottage Museum, Woodhall Spa 01526 353775

Dobson's Windmill, Burgh le Marsh 01754 766658

Dogdyke Pumping Station, Tattershall 01526 342352

Ellis's Windmill, Lincoln 01522 528448

Gayton Drainage Engine, Theddlethorpe All Saints 01754 890209

Heckington Railway Museum, Heckington

Heckington Windmill, Heckington 01529 461919

Louth Museum, Louth 01507 601211

Ludborough Railway Museum, Ludborough 01507 363881

Magdalen Museum, Wainfleet 01754 880343

Manor House Folk Museum, Alford 01507 462143

Mount Pleasant Windmill, Kirton in Lindsey 01652 640177

Museum of Lincolnshire Life, Lincoln 01522 528448

National Fishing Heritage Centre, Grimsby 01472 323345

Normanby Park Farming Museum, Scunthorpe 01724 720588

North Ings Farm Railway, Dorrington 01529 414294

Scunthorpe Museum and Art Gallery, Scunthorpe 01724 843533

Sibsey Trader Windmill, Sibsey 01205 750036

Stamford Museum, Stamford 01789 766317

Stockwith Watermill, Hagworthingham 01507 588221

Tattershall Thorpe Airfield Museum, Tattershall Thorpe 01205 361334

Trolleybus Museum, Sandtoft 01724 711391

Waltham Windmill, Waltham 01472 825368

Wrawby Windmill, Wrawby 01652 653699

**103**

Tollhouses – EL23, 49, LN20, SK29

Warehouses – BN20, EL4, 31, 32, 33, 35, LN2, NK27, NL2, SH6, 22, SK20, WL33, 39, 46

Watermills – EL5, 8, 9, 14, 16, 17, 22, 39, 40, 42, 65, NK12, 13, 24, 26, NL39, SK8, 23, 24, 28, 31, 41, 59, 62, 64, WL11, 12, 13, 27

Water powered pump – NK4

Water Supply – LN5, 32, NK2, 3, 4, 6, 16, 21, SH13, SK2, WL9, 40, 55

Waterwheel – WL15

Wind and Watermill – NL39

Windmills – Millwright's Workshop – EL46

Windmills, Post – NL33

Windmills, Smock – SK4

Windmills, Tower – BN14, 30, EL38, 44, 58, 71, LN15, 34, NE18, NK29, 36, NL21, 39, 41, SH17, 18, 19, WL36, 38

Wind Pumps – EL52

Workhouse – EL13

# INDEX BY PLACE

Gainsborough – WL 40-51
Gayton – See Theddlethorpe EL 21
Grainthorpe – See Austen Fen – EL 4
Grantham – SK 53-61
Greatford – SK 17
Great Limber – WL 18
Grimsby – NE 2-15
Grimsthorpe – See Edenham
Gunby – EL 59

Hagworthingham – EL 65
Hallington – EL 23
Hareby – See Old Bolingbroke EL 66
Harlam Hill – See Bishop Norton WL 32
Harlaxton – SK 51-52
Haverholme – NK 20, See Ewerby
Heapham – WL 36
Heckington – NK 36-38
Hibaldstow – NL 38-40
Hogsthorpe – EL 52
Holbeach – SH 18
Holdingham – NK 22-24
Holton le Moor – WL 22
Horkstow – NL 16
Horncastle – EL 30-38
Humber Bridge – NL 17

Immingham – NE 1
Ingham – WL 35
Ingoldmells – EL 53, See also Addlethorpe

Keadby – NL 6-8
Keddington – EL 6
Ketsby – EL 40
Kirkby Green – NK 13
Kirmington – NL 29
Kirmond le Mire – WL 14
Kirton (near Boston) – BN 29
Kirton in Lindsey – NL 41-44

Langrick – EL 72
Leadenham – NK 42
Lincoln – LN1-34
Little Carlton – EL 22
Little Ponton – SK 46-47
Londonthorpe – See Manthorpe
Long Bennington – SK 44
Long Sutton – SH 19
Louth – EL 7-17
Ludborough – EL 3

Manthorpe – SK 62
Market Deeping – SK 20-22
Market Rasen – WL 27-29
Metheringham – NK 9

Morton (by Bourne) – SK 3
Morton (near Gainsborough) – WL 38-39
Moulton – SH 17

Nettleton – WL 23-24
New Bolingbroke – EL 68-70
New Holland – NL 23-26
Newton on Trent – WL 55
Nocton – NK 7
Normanby le Wold – WL 25
North Hykeham – NK 45-46
North Kyme – NK 18

Old Bolingbroke – EL 66
Old Leake – BN1
Owston Ferry – NL 1-2

Pinchbeck – SH 2-4
Potterhanworth – NK 6

Saltfleet – EL 18-19
Sandtoft – NL 5
Saxilby – WL 56-57
Scopwick – NK 11-12
Scredington – NK 39
Scunthorpe – NL 9-12
Sewstern Lane – SK 44
Sibsey – EL 71
Skegness – EL 54-57
Skellingthorpe – NK 49
Sleaford – NK 25-35
South Ferriby – NL 13-15
South Kelsey – WL 21
South Killingholme – NL 28
South Ormsby – See Ketsby EL 40
South Willingham – EL 27-28
Spalding – SH 5-14
Spilsby – EL 64
Stamford – SK 29-43
Stenigot – EL 25-26
Stixwould – EL 80
Stockwith - See Hagworthingham EL 65
Stow Park – WL 52
Susworth – WL 37
Sutton Bridge – SH 20-26
Sutton on Sea – EL 50
Sutton St Edmunds – SH 28
Swallow – WL 16
Swinderby – NK 43
Swineshead – BN 31

Tallington – SK 25
Tattershall – EL 73-76
Tealby.- WL 11-13
Tetford – EL 39

**105**

Tetney – EL 1-2
Theddlethorpe – EL 20-21
Thoresway – WL 15
Thorpe on the Hill – NK 44
Thorpe St Peter – EL 63
Timberland – NK 14
Torksey – WL 53-54
Tydd St Mary – SH 27

Uffington – SK 26-28

Wainfleet – EL 60-62
Waltham – NE 18
West Deeping – SK 23-24
West Rasen – WL 30
Whisby – NK 47
Wilsford – SK 63
Withcall – EL 24
Woodhall Spa – EL 77-79
Woodnook – See Little Ponton SK 46
Woolsthorpe By Belvoir – SK 48-49
Wrawby – NL 32-33

## ACKNOWLEDGEMENTS

Various members of the Industrial Archaeology Group of the Society for Lincolnshire History and Archaeology have contributed information and photographs for this Guide, particularly, Roger Audis, Barrie Barton, Ken Hollamby, Chris Lester, Simon Pawley, Ken Redmore, Jon Sass, Stuart Squires, Peter Stevenson, John Turner, Sarah Wright and Neil Wright. To all these and to others whose previous publications have provided information, the Editor is grateful, but the errors and omissions are his own.

## PHOTOGRAPHIC CREDITS

The pictures which illustrate this booklet come from several sources and identifying initials appear in each caption. The key is as follows:

CJL – Chris Lester

FHM – Friends of Heckington Mill

JAS – Jon Sass

KH – Ken Hollamby

KR – Ken Redmore

NRW – Neil Wright

PS – Peter Stevenson

SES – Stewart Squires

SJW – Sarah Wright

JT – John Turner